JEAN IN THE MORNING

JEAN IN
THE MORNING

★

JANET SANDISON

*(Janet Sandison is the pseudonym of Jane Duncan,
author of the 'My Friend' sequence of novels)*

THE
COMPANION BOOK CLUB
LONDON

This edition is published by
The Hamlyn Publishing Group Ltd.
and is issued by arrangement with
Macmillan and Co. Ltd.

Jean in the Morning is the first of
a four-novel sequence under the general title of
'An Apology for the Life of Jean Robertson'

*The author and publisher wish to
thank the copyright holders of the hymns
quoted in the text*

GIFT

*Made and printed in Great Britain
for the Companion Book Club
by Odhams (Watford) Ltd.*
600771229
600871223

CHAPTER ONE

Jesus loves me! this I know,
For the Bible tells me so;
Little ones to Him belong;
They are weak, but He is strong.

HYMN 660

WHEN I WAS FIVE YEARS OLD I went to school and the very first thing I learned was 'Jesus loves me'. At first I was very much afraid of school because it was new and everything new was frightening. I went there on the first day with a big girl called Maisie Anderson who lived upstairs from us and she led me in through the iron gates in the wall with the iron railings on top, across the concrete playground and into the grey stone building to a big room which had dark brown paint half-way up the walls, a lot of long wooden forms with desks in front of them and there was a queer dry stale smell. Maisie led me to a high desk that stood all alone in the middle of the floor and here there was a lady, sitting on a high chair with a pen in her hand and a big book in front of her. She had a thin face, spectacles that pinched her nose and she looked down at me sternly and said: 'Name?'

'Tell your name,' Maisie whispered and gave me a prod in the back.

'Jean Robertson,' I said and the pen scratched in the book.

'Address?' the lady said now. I did not know what she meant.

'Where do you live?' she asked impatiently.

'Railway Terrace, miss,' said Maisie.

'Number?' the teacher asked Maisie now.

'Same close as me but down the stair,' said Maisie.

'Down the stair *what*?' said the teacher very sternly.

'Miss,' said Maisie.

'Which side?'

Maisie looked up at the ceiling and I knew that she was imagining herself standing at the mouth of our close. She held out her right hand.

'Number three,' said the teacher, scratching with the pen again and then to me: 'Go and sit over there and no talking. Next. Name?'

That was how I found out what an address was and what my own address was so perhaps that was the first thing I learned at school and not 'Jesus loves me' but 'Jesus loves me' must have been the second thing.

After all the names and addresses had been scratched into the book the teacher said that if there was any more fidgeting or talking she would strap every one of us and that we were to pay attention because we were going to learn 'Jesus loves me'. After that, every morning, school began with 'Jesus loves me' and the people who could not say it by themselves on Friday morning got the strap. I did not get the strap because I could say it. I had been able to say it on Tuesday, the very first day but, of course, I did not know what it meant. I had never heard of Jesus; I had never heard of love and I had never heard of the Bible and this lesson that came first every morning was called 'Bible'. To the best of my knowledge, I belonged to my mother and father and not to Jesus and although I was said to be little for my age, I was not weak but quite healthy, probably as strong for my age as Jesus.

On the way home that first day, I recited to Maisie Anderson the words I had learned but before I could ask her what they meant she said: 'Ach, you and your old Bible! When you've been at the school as long as me, you'll be sick o' Bible,' and with this she ran away to join some bigger girls, leaving me to find my own way home. And so, that day or a day or two later, I came to know that school things like Bible and spelling and two-times table were only for inside

6

school and not to be mentioned outside and that school itself was only something that had to be put up with until you were fourteen and could leave it for good. This knowledge, unlike 'Jesus loves me,' was comprehensible to me for life was made up, in the main, of things that had to be put up with and these things were called your circumstances. According to my mother, some people had very good circumstances while the circumstances of others were poor. I found my own on the poor side, especially this new one called school.

The best thing about school was the playground, where we went for what was called 'Interval' in the forenoon and for interval again in the afternoon and we also spent some time there after we had been released from school for the day. It was quite like the backyard at Railway Terrace, being concrete with a wall all round it and having the lean-to row of water closets at the end, just like the wash-houses in the Terrace yard but it was better than the yard at the Terrace because you could run all the way across it without bumping into a clothes-pole. The backyard at the Terrace was like a forest of iron trees, with all the iron poles sticking up to hold the ropes for drying the washing.

It seemed to me that I learned a great deal more in the playground than I learned in the classroom—important things, at any rate. It was in the playground that I learned about Lochfoot, which was the address of the town where I lived. In a way, I had always known that our town was called Lochfoot and that if you went down to the station and got into the train, which I had never done, you could go right down-the-line to Glasgow, but I did not really know *about* Lochfoot until after a few weeks in the school playground. There, I learned that Lochfoot was made up of several different groups of people. In the playground, the first group was the Villagers, children whose homes were in the old Village which was a row of houses along one side of a loop of road, quite near yet quite separate from the rest of the town. The second group was the Railies, children whose fathers worked on the railway and who lived, mostly, in Railway Terrace, where I lived; next came the Trammies, children whose fathers worked on the tramcars or at the Tramway Depot and who lived in Tramway Buildings and last came the Tinkers, children of the old tinker clans, once nomadic but now squatted for most of the year in ramshackle roystering near-permanence in a smoky rash of caravans, tents and shacks round the old dam, away beyond the outskirts of the town. Villagers, Railies and Trammies approached the school gates by the same road while the Tinkers came from the opposite direction, from the direction where no townsfolk ever went because it led away into unknown territory of moors, lochs and hills.

Although the four divisions were there, though, they blurred a little at the edges in some cases, like the blue stuff your mother put into the rinsing water for the pillow slips, melting down from a dark blob in the clear water until you could not see its edges at all. Villagers included children who came from the lodges and cottages up at the Castle and also old Beery-belly the policeman's Minnie and old Loco the station-master's Willie. Railies included the Co-op shopman's daughter and the butcher's son. Trammies included the Antonios, the children of the Italian fish and chip man and I myself was, I thought, a very interesting blur on the line dividing Villagers from Railies, because I had a granny who was 'Castle folk' and lived in the Village.

It was during the first days of September in the year 1911 that I learned the words 'Jesus loves me' but I cannot tell the exact dates when I learned many other things, such as that Jesus was the son of God and lived up in Heaven and that the Devil was waiting down in Hell to throw you into his fire at the first opportunity. I was, however, more interested in Jesus than in the Devil because Jesus was so very unusual.

That Jesus should love me and all other children meant that he must be a most unusual person for everybody knew that

8

children were just an expense and a nuisance. They had to be clothed and fed and they tramped into the newly-scrubbed close with their dirty feet and they were for ever banging the door of the water closet or leaving it standing open so that anybody who came to the close-mouth could see that vulgar It staring them in the face. I do not know, either, when I discovered what love was but I came to know that, except in connection with Jesus, it was very dirty, wicked and secretive, a word that was never heard but seen, only, scratched in chalk on the wall behind the playground water closets. 'Willie loves Minnie.' 'Jackie loves Cathie.' If people were caught writing these things, they got a proper licking from old Cock the Headmaster because they were so wicked and dirty and disgusting. Jesus, however, was different. You were not only allowed to say that he loved you, you were forced to say it and sing it too, at the pitch of your voice and if you did not say it and sing it, the strap came stinging across the palms of your hands.

In my early days at school, before I learned not to say out loud any of the things inside my head—before I had been at school for long enough to learn anything at all, that is—I said to some of the other girls that I just did not believe in this Jesus who loved us all and a very strange and frightening thing happened. They all drew away from me, their eyes round with horror, as if I had suddenly the power to kill them all and it was only when I began to cry with fright that one of them summoned the courage to say in a low whisper: 'Jeanie Robertson, if you say things like that you'll go straight down to Hell!'

After that, I did not say anything more to anybody about Jesus but I continued to find it difficult to believe in him. It was much easier to believe in the Devil because he was so much more natural, more like the other people I knew. His hell-fire was much the same, only more so, than a slapping from your mother or the teacher's strap or Beery-belly the policeman's

9

prison. And his hell where you could be shut up for ever and ever could only be rather like the brown-walled classroom or the brick-walled backyard at the Terrace, except that it had a fire in it. It was easier to believe in Hell and the fire than it was to believe in Heaven away up above the sky where the sun shone for ever and ever around the throne of God.

Still, with Bible every morning from Monday to Friday at school and Sunday school on Sundays, one heard so much about Jesus that it was impossible not to think of him now and then and at some stage I arrived at the conclusion that what made him so difficult to believe in was that he dealt in souls, which were invisible, if they existed at all, while the Devil dealt in bodies, liking to burn them in his fire and bodies were visible. Lochfoot was full of bodies, as many as fourteen to two rooms in some houses. There was plenty of hell-fuel in Lochfoot but of the number of souls for Jesus to love I was less sure. It seemed very likely that souls were reserved for people who had plenty of money, like the cream cakes in the baker's window and clothes that were new and not your mother's old skirt made over.

However, the souls-business made Jesus and his love for children more comprehensible. Souls had no feet and no need for water closets so Jesus, up in Heaven, would not be 'harassed to death' with his children tramping in through the close with dirty feet or leaving open the door of the water closet. And if, perchance, one had a soul, it was good to know that somebody loved it and in course of time, perhaps, I might discover whether or not I had one. When I considered that Heaven had no need of water closets, it did seem to be the 'happy land far far away' of another hymn that we had to learn because water closets, in Railway Terrace, caused more trouble than any other one thing except children.

In the Terrace, there were fifteen closes, which were con-crete-floored passages leading to an iron-railed stone staircase and each close had a house on either side downstairs and a house on either side of the landing upstairs. In the middle of this landing, there was a door to a water closet and down below, under the stairs, there was another door to another water closet. Upstairs, above us, Maisie Anderson, who had taken me to school for the first time, lived with her parents and her brothers; in the other house upstairs lived the Fergusons and their four boys and they all used the upstairs water closet. Down below, across the close from us, old Miss Miller lived with her older brother who was a railway guard and they shared the downstairs water closet with us.

You come to know things in a very mixed-up roundabout way and it was because of the upstairs water closet that I came to know that my granny down in the village was not really my granny at all. This was away back, before I went to school. My father had just come in from work in the railway siding one day and he, my mother and I were just going to have our dinner when my mother said: 'The closet up the stair was blocked again this morning. Goodness knows what that woman Anderson puts down it. If I am not sick of clearing up other folks' dirt! Running down the stair, it was, into the close.'

'Has the plumber been?' my father asked.

'Aye, but he never cleans up the mess and it's down *my* side of the close it comes, never down that uppish Miss Miller's side. I never thought to live in a place like this,' she complained, as she often did. As a rule, at these times, my father merely drew in a long breath, finished his meal and went back to work but on this day he said: 'It's your own doing that we're living here. We could still be in the Village with my mother if you had contented yourself.'

'She's *not* your mother, the old bizzom!' my mother said fiercely. 'She was only a second wife, that's all. And the Castle had no right to put us out of the Village and let her stop on.'

'She was a mother to *me*,' my father said, 'and the Castle has every right to do what it likes with its houses. And my mother was Castle folk herself before she married my father.

I have no right to the cottage and neither have you. Railie folk don't get Castle houses and that's the end o' it.'

The conversation now ended, as these conversations always did, with my father finishing his meal, reaching for his cap and going away back to the railway siding while my mother, frowning angrily, washed the few dishes in the bowl in the sink.

Another thing to be learned from these conversations that began with the upstairs water closet was that my mother would have liked to live in the Village, but there was nothing unusual in that. Most people in Lochfoot would have liked to live in the Village if they could.

Each house in the Village was quite separate from every other house and when you went in through my granny's front door, having opened the gate that said 'Lilac Cottage' and having gone along the path between the small plots of flowers, there was a stair going up but the house upstairs belonged to my granny too and not to another family like the Andersons. In my granny's house, there was a water closet under the stairs too but it was all her own and she did not share it with anybody like Miss Miller. But it was not just because of having a garden and your own water closet that everybody wanted to live in the Village. It was because of a thing that I came to know on my sixth birthday.

My mother did not like me to go to see my granny. I did not understand why this was because my mother did not want me 'for ever under her feet' and was always telling me to go outside and play but if she knew that I went to see my granny she was always very angry, although my granny did not seem to object to me being under her feet, sitting on the fender stool at Lilac Cottage. I knew that if you disobeyed your mother the Devil would get you when you died and take you down to Hell to burn you for ever and ever and although this was very frightening to think about, I sometimes disobeyed my mother nevertheless and went down to the Village to see my granny. I always went when I was very hungry, which was fairly often, but I could not go so frequently after I started school.

So, on the Saturday morning just after my sixth birthday, I went down to the Village and as I skipped along to the tune of one of my school hymns, it occurred to me that if I was six and Maisie Anderson was ten, probably all the other people in the world had an age too, even my mother, even my granny. But a question about ages was not the sort of question to ask my mother. In fact, my mother was always too busy to be bothered with questions and her reply always was: 'Ach, hold your tongue and get out o' my road.' When I went into Lilac Cottage, my granny was sitting by her fire as usual and I told her I was six now and she said: 'A big girl, old enough to make a cup o' tea for her granny. Go and fill the kettle.'

With pride, I filled the kettle at the tap and set it on the fire to boil while I fetched the cups from the dresser and a thick slice of bread spread with jam for myself. My mother never allowed me even to touch our kettle or to open the door of our cupboard. She said that I would only make a mess and that when I began to eat I did not know when to stop and would have her eaten out of house and home if I got my own way. When we were drinking the tea, I said: 'Granny, how old are you?'

She laughed her seldom little laugh and then she said: 'Old enough to mind on when Railway Terrace an' Tramway Buildin's was a green field.'

I did not stay with her for very long that day because I wanted to be alone to think of this miraculous time, long ago, when there had been no Railway Terrace, no Tramway Buildings, no iron clothes-poles, no brick walls round the backyards, only a green field and in the end I made up my mind that my mother, all the Railies and all the Trammies would like to live in the Village because the houses there could remember that long-ago time of the green field.

Tramway Buildings ran along one side of the one-time green field, the side that was nearest to the town, the railway station and the tramway depot. Then, at the corner of the field, there was a dark alleyway between the back of Tramway Buildings and the end of Railway Terrace. Coming along Railway Terrace to the next corner, there was an alleyway between it and the Co-op shop and down the third side of the field, joined on to the Co-op, was the pub, Gardiner the Cobbler's shop and one or two others before you came to the stone wall that encircled old Pillans's place.

Old Pillans's place was creepy, like old Pillans himself. Later on, I found out that it had once been a farmhouse, the area encircled by the wall had once been a barnyard and there were still some outbuildings round at the back. It was very old, older even than the Village but it was not a farm any more. No fowls clucked in the barnyard which was now full of a tangled mass of rusty iron—old wheels, old iron bed-steads, bits and pieces of railings—and the house in the middle was a rectangular block of grey stone with a lot of boarded-up windows like blind eyes.

Old Pillans lived there all alone when he was not creeping down the roadside close to the wall to catch the tramcar that would take him to Glasgow. The adjective 'old' as we school-children used it had no connection with age, of course. We applied it to anyone in authority who, automatically because of the authority, we did not like. Its application to Pillans, however, was no concession to authority as vested in Mr. Cockburn or old Cock, the schoolmaster, or as vested in the uniforms of old Beery-belly the policeman, old Loco the station-master or old Squeak the tramways superintendent. Pillans had no uniform other than a greasy bowler hat and a long drooping black overcoat which he wore all the year round but he had an obscure evil authority of which we children were all aware although he never spoke to us. He owned the town's pawnshop where women took carpets or anything they could spare when their husbands had drunk the weekly pay packet. This shop was known as 'the Second-hand' for, although in theory it was a pawnshop, few articles that went in through its front door in exchange for a few pennies were ever redeemed. They remained to be sold again at a high profit.

Old Pillans's place, then, occupied the corner of the erstwhile green field and round this corner on the fourth side, over the wall, the field was bounded by the Burn. When the field had been a field and was not covered with buildings and concrete backyards and high dividing walls of brick, when old Pillans's place had been a farm, the Burn had been a clean stream flowing along and into the big conduit pipe at Pillans's corner which took it under the road and out round the Village to join the loch. Nowadays, it was a black, rat-infested stinking sewer, for all the water closets of Tramway Buildings, Railway Terrace, the pub, the shops and old Pillans's place discharged into it, through pipes in the brick walls that enclosed the various backyards.

On the other side of the Burn there was a narrow strip of sickly, slimy grey-green grass out of which rose the twelve-foot wall of mason-hewn stone, overhung by the lush branches of beeches and oaks, which formed the barrier between Lochfoot Castle and the world outside.

The heirarchy of the school playground, Villagers, Railies, Trammies and Tinkers was not representative of the whole of Lochfoot. Outside the playground, there were three further strata of society. The first of these was of no interest to the child world although of great interest to my mother. It was a piece of road at the back of the town, under the wall of the manse garden, called Victoria Drive, a road that suddenly ended and turned into fields, but it did not end for good, because just after I went to school, some men came and made it a little bit longer before more men came and began to build another house beside it.

15

'There's another house going up in Victoria Drive,' I told my mother, repeating the school news of the day.

'Aye, old Jamieson the Draper's,' she said, disappointingly knowing my news already. 'He's made a right pile for himself in the shop.' She was talking as much to herself as to me now, as she often did. 'Mind you, his father left him a good bit. They have aye been in good circumstances, the Jamiesons.'

This then, I came to know, was what Victoria Drive was, the place lived in by retired folk in good circumstances and it was of no interest to us children because no children lived there, but the other two strata were different.

Far, far distant from all the children of the playground and their parents was the world of Lochview Crescent, a world as far away from Railway Terrace as Buckingham Palace is from some garden suburb. This was an area above the banks of the loch which had been colonized by Glasgow businessmen. They had covered it with solid, grey Victorian villas in large gardens and from here they commuted daily by train to Glasgow and sent their children to fee-paying schools in the city or to boarding-schools further afield. Marvellous tales were told in the school playground of the grandeurs of Lochview by the butcher's son and the baker's daughter who went up there with their fathers on Saturdays to help with the deliveries. But even Lochview, with its lawns, gravel drives, marble doorsteps and bathrooms could not stand comparison with the Castle. If Lochview was to Railway Terrace what Buckingham Palace is to a garden suburb, the Castle to the rest, including Lochview, was as God. I knew that the Castle, like God, was there although I had never seen it and, like God unseen, it impinged daily on my life and the lives of my fellows and, indeed, bounded them. You could not walk for more than a mile in any direction from the railway station on the outskirts of Lochfoot without coming, bang, against the twelve-foot, mason-built wall that surrounded the Castle and its grounds. At four different points, this wall gave way to even taller iron gates which were always closed and inside each there was a little lodge with a well-tended garden, neat curtains at the windows and an air of shut-in uncontaminable superiority. With your mind, you knew that people lived in these lodges, you knew, even, that some of your schoolfellows lived there—in the playground they ranked as Villagers—but the doors of these houses were never open, nobody moved around them, you could see no washing flapping in the breeze in their back gardens. When you looked through the iron bars of the gates, there was only the silence that prevailed beyond the barrier, the lace-curtain-blinded lodge windows and the long curving sweep of the drive disappearing into the long green tunnel of the overhanging trees. In the classroom at school, we were given the impression that the Castle, like God, was a 'good thing' and although I and, no doubt, some of my fellows thought sometimes that neither the Castle nor God seemed to do much to make manifest their essential goodness, we accepted both without rebellion because they were authorities so remote that we dumbly recognized them as being utterly beyond our compass.

No other authority in Lochfoot went unchallenged by us, however. The uniform of Beery-belly was a matter for derision, as were those of Loco and Squeak and we raided the territory of the latter two, breaking windows and stealing anything we could carry, until we were chased hooting away by the former. Our only form of communication with the rest of the world and largely, also, between ourselves was what was known as giving 'cheek.' We gave cheek to our parents, our teachers and to authority in all its forms and long before I went to school I knew that this was the position of the child *vis-à-vis* the rest of the world. The world held you down in an iron and concrete grip of railings, walled yards and stern discipline against which your only redress was the giving of cheek. It was only after I went to school, however, that I learned that the giving of cheek extended to a world beyond that of parents,

17

teachers and the wearers of petty uniforms. It was at school that I learned that the whole world was a battleground where the weak went to the wall, a battleground where the giving of cheek was a puny weapon that made little impression but one went on wielding it because it was the only weapon one had.

In the playground, in the backyards and on the road to and from school, we of the child tribe spent much time fighting among ourselves but occasionally a queer thing would happen. Suddenly, usually on a Saturday afternoon, the air above the backyard of Railway Terrace or Tramway Buildings would grow still, the brick boundary walls would hang waiting and then, as if it arose out of the ground, there would come a cry of: 'Up Lochview!' and one would at once be invaded by a feeling of warm gay comradeship, a solidarity of companionship as one was caught up in a glow of high adventurous endeavour. In a shouting, laughing disorderly rabble, we would take to the road that led from the town centre to Lochview Crescent, arming ourselves as we went with sticks from the wayside hedges and stones from the ditches until we came to the corner where the villas and gardens of the Crescent began.

As a member of the tribe, I used to feel the breathless warmth of high endeavour but at the same time I knew that to a spectator we were now a yelling destructive mob as we went crashing down the curve of the road between the gardens into the drawn-blinds afternoon silence, shoving open gates that were closed, banging shut gates that were open, breaking the glass of street lamps with stones, slashing at trees and shrubs with our sticks and all the time shouting not words but fierce animal cries. If a horrified householder came into sight on his doorstep or behind her window-pane, we became more savage still and derisory too, some of the boys putting their thumbs to their noses, some of the girls turning their backs and cocking up their skirts to expose dirty deriding knickers to the respectable invaded citizenry until there would come a cry

18

of 'Old Beery-belly!' and, dropping our weapons, we would all take to our heels and scatter in all directions, to make our way by devious routes back to our own territory while the police constable descended, puffing, from his bicycle to survey the carnage left by our passing.

The next day, there would be a lecture at school from old Cock, a visit by old Beery-belly to various parents but none of us who had taken part in the raid spoke a word to one another about what we had done on the day before. And, strangely, after an 'up Lochview' there was comparative peace among the factions in the playground. It was as if a pressure had built up among us Railie and Trammie children, a pressure that war against the Villagers and Tinkers could not release, so that we had to take measures more extreme to obtain alleviation.

I was to learn later that even the Castle was not immune to our depredations but there was one man in Lochfoot whom we never attacked in any way, one man who was allowed to pass by on the road without so little as a derisory hoot from any child. This man was old Pillans. Although his house stood empty all day while he was at the Second-hand or in Glasgow and although we had to pass it four times a day on our way to school, home for dinner, back to school and home again in the afternoon, never was a stone thrown at its boarded-up windows and never did anyone go through the gap in the wall where no gate hung. We would stop at the corner where the sewer ran under the road and drop a few stones over into the murky water and then in silence we would run past old Pillans's place, only beginning to squabble and give cheek to one another again when we came to the end of his wall and were passing by Gardiner the Cobbler's shop.

And if, on our way to school or anywhere about the town, we saw Pillans coming towards us, we crossed to the other side of the road or street and stood still, quiet and close together until he had passed by; while to discover that he had come

19

out of his house as you passed and was coming along the road behind you was a thing that set you running as fast as you could until you came to a place such as the pub close, where you ran in and waited in silence and watchfully until Pillans had gone out of sight.

He always walked close to the wall at the side of the road, his head in its greasy bowler hat bent forward, his eyes on the ground, his long black overcoat flapping about his shins. He looked at nobody and spoke to nobody as he walked along, wrapped in his queer invisible veil of secrecy. As a rule, we passed his pawnshop in a similar silent way as we passed his house but, sometimes, he was in the doorway of the shop or on the pavement in front of it, buying a piece of carpet from a woman or supervising the unloading from a lorry of some old furniture he had had sent down from Glasgow. At these times, you stood silent, at a safe distance and watched, not because you wanted to but because you could not help it. You did not want to see Pillans running his strangely long and prehensile fingers over Mrs. Guthrie the Railie's hearthrug before forcing her to let him have it for sixpence instead of the shilling that she needed. You did not want to watch him running his sharp close-together eyes over the pathetic sticks that the lorrymen were unloading but, unwilling as you were, you had to stand there, as if rooted to the ground by some evil fascination until, at last, there came the blissful moment of release when Pillans disappeared into the dark cavern of his shop and your feet were free to move again. Suddenly, you were running, looking for something to kick, something to destroy and you knocked the bucket of cod-heads outside the fish shop into the gutter or brought down with a crash the string of tin pans that hung outside the ironmonger's.

Once, on the way home from school at dinner-time, we were passing old Pillans's house and a terrible thing happened. We did what we never usually did but we did it not of our own will. We looked up at one of the high boarded windows of the house and today there were no boards on it. Instead, Pillans was there in the aperture, looking down at us. We all stopped moving and stood there, looking up. It was the first time I had ever seen his face fully for, on the road or at his pawnshop, he always wore his hat, pulled down low over his eyes and ears. It was a small, thin pale face with dark eyebrows and dark hair except for the greyish-white scalp above his forehead where he was going bald. He wore a dark grey shirt with no collar and over it a black garment known as a sleeved waistcoat, the body of which was made of black worsted stuff and the sleeves of shiny black lining material. He was very thin, with arms that seemed to be disproportionately long and as he looked down at us from the window frame, his position was curiously contorted. His left arm, in its shiny black tight sleeve, came right across the front of his body so that the hand gripped the bottom of the window frame on his right side and his right arm, in the other shiny tight black sleeve was held above his head, the hand gripping the top of the window frame. The thin white face looking down from among the shiny black coils of the uncannily prehensile arms made me think of a snake, still, watchful, malevolent, ready to strike.

After what seemed to be a long time, he moved, drawing up from inside the framework of wooden boards and fixing it in the window aperture, hiding himself from our sight and thus releasing us. As if we were controlled by a single brain and a single system of motor nerves, we rushed up the road, past the cobbler's shop and the pub, past our homes in the Terrace and the Buildings and indulged in an orgy of doorbell ringing along the main street of the town. It was not a proper 'bell-ringing' within the child tribe's rules for this activity. It was a debauched disorganized orgy in which nobody cared whether they were identified as bell-ringers or not which was a blatant transgression of the basic rule of this game. Indeed, it was not a bell-ringing at all. It was a thing without a name.

Bell-ringing was not a dinner-time game in any case. Bell

ringing was for the late summer twilight or for the long cold winter evenings. The main street of the town that ran down to the railway station and the tramway depot had two-storey buildings on either side, some of them houses occupied by more senior railway or tramway officials, some of them shops, with flats above where their owners lived. There were also two public houses and the church in this street. The church porch opened on to the pavement between the fishmonger's and the fish and chip shop.

All these houses and flats had polished brass doorbells and our pastime was to ring these bells and run away. It took at least three years' apprenticeship to become a really praiseworthy bell-ringer, for merely to ring the bell and run was not enough. You had to commit the full nuisance of bringing the householder downstairs to the door to give full satisfaction to the tribe and it took courage to listen to the bell ring inside, listen to the menacing footsteps of authority coming nearer and nearer down the stairs and along the passage and wait for the door to open before, with a loud jeering laugh, you ran away into the yelling crowd that came rushing along the street to cover your identity in retreat. In the twilight of summer or the dark of winter, the back of one ragged boy or girl looked very much like another and old Beery-belly had long since given up any attempt to identify illicit bell-ringers. I had begun my apprenticeship as a bell-ringer before I went to school, but after a few months of school education, it was generally conceded that I was very good at bells and, at last, the evening came when I obtained my equivalent of the baccalaureate by ringing old Poopit's bell at the door of the manse and getting out of the grounds again, uncaught by him, his wife, his gardener and four servants.

The minister, known as 'Poopit' because this was Lochfoot dialect for 'pulpit', received treatment as derisory but slightly different to that meted out to the rest of the population. You did not shout 'Old Poopit!' after him in daytime as you shouted 'Old Beery-belly!' at the policeman when he passed you on his bicycle. In daylight, you treated Poopit with silence, although you did not flee to put distance between him and yourself as you did when you met Pillans. If you met Pillans after dark, too, you ran for your life while if you met Poopit, you began to follow him at a little distance, making cat-calls and shouting, 'Hi, old Poopit, how's your missus?'

After I had been a full school-going member of the child tribe for some time, I discovered that everything we said and did had its reason, however obscure, that all the customs of tribal culture were rooted very deep. This particular call for the parish minister was undoubtedly rooted in the fact that at Sunday school and on Prize Days he was always telling us that we were sinners, that all children were born in sin and he told us these things in the face of our knowledge that he had eight children of his own. They did not come to our school, of course, but caught the daily train to Glasgow but we knew of their existence and our after-dark enquiries as to the health of Poopit's wife were no more nor less than a delicate reference to his own after-dark sins.

In daylight, we treated Poopit to silence because he looked different from other men, always clean, with his soft pudgy hands, black clothes and white back-to-front collar but after dark, somehow, he became like other men and although God was reputed to see everything and know everything, it was just possible that, in the dark, even he could not identify which child among so many had raised the cry: 'Hi, old Poopit, how's your missus?'

Except for Bible and old Pillans, life was completely comprehensible to me when I was six years old. It was full of trials like feeling hungry and having to go to school but these were reasonable understandable things. You were hungry because your mother was saving up so that one day she would be in better circumstances and it was hard to save when your father spent so much money on getting drunk every Saturday night and you were sent to school and Sunday school to be 'out of the road' while your mother got on with her work during the week and had a little peace from your noise on Sunday afternoons. But Bible and old Pillans were not reasonable and understandable. Pillans was a hideous creepy crawly mystery and Bible was enough to knock you downright stupid, especially when you thought of Jesus loving you and saying, 'Suffer little children to come unto me.' What could this mean?

I knew about suffering. Your mother said: 'I've just scrubbed that water closet and if you tramp in there with your dirty feet, you'll suffer for it,' and the teacher said: 'And if you can't say the whole of Jesus loves me by Friday, you'll suffer for it!' Did Jesus mean that he wanted the children to come because he liked to suffer the way he suffered when he was crucified? Or did he mean that if the children came, he would make them suffer? But then there was the hymn:

> *Jesus loves me! this I know,*
> *For the Bible tells me so;*
> *Little ones to Him belong;*
> *They are weak, but He is strong.*

That sounded as if Jesus was really different from everybody else and truly wanted children to belong to him.

It was all very confusing but of no real importance compared with the struggle for survival, the holding of one's place in the tribe from day to day and the hymn was all right, in its way. It was a useful tune for skipping to or for humming inside your head in bed in winter to help you to forget how cold and hungry you were until you went to sleep.

CHAPTER TWO

There's a home for little children
Above the bright blue sky,
HYMN 593

QUITE EARLY IN MY LIFE I came to know, although I do not know how, that when my mother and father had first married, my father had been a ploughman in the service of the Home Farm, which belonged to the Castle, and he had taken his bride, my mother, home to live in the Village, at Lilac Cottage, with my granny. Such an arrangement was common in the Village. Many of the cottages had a granny or a grandpa in them, as well as a mother and father and children but there were no grannies or grandpas in Railway Terrace or Tramway Buildings, possibly because there was no room for them but more probably because these tenements were occupied largely by Highland and Irish immigrants to Lochfoot. In the case of my granny and my father and mother, however, the arrangement had not worked and very early in my life I understood in an unformulated way why it had not worked.

My mother liked being married instead of being an old maid like Miss Miller next door and she would have liked to live in the Village when my father took her there but the trouble was that, although she liked the Village house and the weekly pay packet that marriage brought, she did not like people 'under her feet,' people like my granny and me. Best of all, my mother liked the weekly pay packet and she had not been married for very long before she discovered that a ploughman's pay packet did not hold as much as a railway labourer's. Instead of a lot of money, a ploughman was paid partly in things like sacks of potatoes, oatmeal, milk and firewood but my mother was not interested in these things.

She was interested in money which you could save, until, one day, you would be in better circumstances so, in the end, she persuaded my father to turn into a railway labourer. It was then that the Castle sent my granny a letter saying that she must not have railway employees at Lilac Cottage, because the rooms should be available if required for unmarried men of the Castle staff. The rooms, though, were never required and my granny always lived alone with no lodgers while we lived at Railway Terrace and somehow my mother came to think that it was my granny's fault that we had to live in the Terrace instead of in the Village. This was why she often called my granny an old bizzom and did not like me to go to see her.

My mother, however, did not intend to go on living in the Terrace. She looked upon our house there only as a place for waiting in until she would be rich enough to leave it. She intended to get rich through a thing called her 'economy,' which meant that we had skimmed milk with our porridge, potatoes and herring for our dinner, bread and jam for our tea and hardly ever had a fire in the grate.

Our house consisted of two rooms, the kitchen and the parlour. The kitchen contained a small black coal-burning range which was highly polished all the time with no ashes lying around, a chipped sink under the window, a cupboard with shelves in a corner and a built-in wooden bunker for coal which was usually empty. If we ever had a fire, it was of wood stamped 'surplus to requirement' which my father brought home from the railway siding. The movable furniture consisted of a wooden table and four wooden chairs that were always scrubbed white and had no grease stains or crumbs on them, an iron double bedstead in which my parents slept and my bed which folded up into an upholstered armchair during the day.

Aside from these items, there were two white wooden joiner-made boxes of the kind called 'kists' which were made for the storage of blankets. One of these held the clothing which we were not wearing, the cupboard held our food, crockery and utensils and the second kist was always locked. The kists were draped with turkey-red cotton and you could sit on them if you were so inclined.

Our parlour was a masterpiece of economy. The parlours of Railway Terrace looked out over the street, the wall with their windows rising directly out of the pavement and if you passed along there, you passed a series of rectangles of glass behind which were lace curtains, looped back with ribbons— the ribbons on ours were pink—to form an upside-down V and in each V there was a small table, draped with a cloth on which sat an aspidistra in a fancy china pot. What nobody except my father, my mother and I knew was that our parlour contained the curtains, the table, the aspidistra and nothing else. My mother, as she often said, knew what was what and she was not going to spend money on a room that we never used, beyond screening the window so that we could not be overlooked, for to allow yourself to be overlooked was vulgar. Mrs. Murphy, who lived further along the Terrace, had no navy blue blind on her kitchen window and when the light was on in winter, you could look in and see her nursing her baby in the most vulgar way, among all her untidiness and clutter, not minding a bit about being overlooked.

My mother 'kept herself to herself' and nobody ever came to our house for a gossip because this would have led to the providing of a cup of tea and even a biscuit and the only person she spoke to was Miss Miller who lived across the close from us in Number One. My mother, in the parlance of the child tribe, was 'in it' with Miss Miller. This meant that there was a relationship between them for to be in it with someone was the only form of relationship that we knew. The idiom was taken, probably, from our arch-enemy, authority, for when some damage had been done, such as a window broken by a thrown stone, old Cock or old Beery-belly or whoever the representative of authority might be would say: 'I want the truth now or I'll belt the lot of you. Who was in it?' Thus, in my mind, my mother and Miss Miller were in something together—there was a relationship of sorts between them. They did not like one another. Indeed, they disliked one another more than anything but neither of them could ignore the other as both of them could ignore Mrs. Anderson and Mrs. Ferguson upstairs.

It seemed to me at this time that the world was made up of a large number of individual units who were all at war with one another, except for myself and my granny. I was 'in it' with my granny in a queer secret way that I could not explain to myself, so that sometimes there would be between us a bond that spanned her hearthrug like a strand of beautiful silken thread. At these times, although I was sitting two yards away from her, I felt as if I were part of her and she were part of me.

Gradually, I became aware of my mother and Miss Miller being in it but it was not the silken beautiful thing that some-times connected my granny and me that was between them. It was more like the double-curved snake-like hooks with points at both ends on which the meat hung in the butcher's shop. One point was stuck into my mother, the other into Miss Miller, holding them unwillingly together while they both strove constantly to detach the other and cast her down on to the bloody sawdust of the shop floor.

Before I went to school, this relationship between my mother and Miss Miller was the only one I had had the oppor-tunity to observe, except for the queer 'quietness,' as I called it inside my head, between my father and my mother. In the time before I went to school, if Miss Miller had been particu-larly irritating, my mother would relieve her feelings by talking aloud about her in my hearing. The words were not addressed to me, however. My mother was talking to herself and anybody in the backyard would tell you that only 'dafties' talked to themselves, so when my mother did this it was very frightening.

I used, therefore, to break in on her self-communings with some comment, to make it feel as if she and I were talking together and one day I said: 'But Miss Miller is a good neighbour, isn't she?' That people were good or bad neighbours was one of the clichés of Railway Terrace. I was not sure what the phrase meant but it had the comfort of familiarity.

'Her a neighbour?' my mother said sharply. 'She's just—ach, she's just one o' the—the *circumstances* o' this place. Hold your tongue and go out and play.'

This was how I discovered that the people around you as well as the places and things around you were part of your circumstances, that favourite word of my mother's, the longest grandest-sounding word in her vocabulary.

Miss Miller was, in my mother's word, uppish. She lived with her bachelor brother who was a railway guard and with his good pay and no children to eat them out of house and home, Miss Miller was very uppish indeed, so uppish that, one time, she made my mother spend a whole shilling. Miss Miller did not know that she had done this and my mother would never have admitted that Miss Miller could have made her spend a shilling but this was what happened all the same. It was very queer how somebody could do something without knowing they had done it or without meaning to do it but there it was.

Miss Miller had a sister who was in very good circumstances, married to a very rich man who had a butcher's shop in Glasgow and one Christmas—the Christmas before I went to school—this sister sent Miss Miller a new china pot for her aspidistra although, as my mother said, Miss Miller having an aspidistra pot already, a second one was just pure vulgar uppishness. The vulgar uppishness was so unbearable that, the next day, my mother went down to old Pillans's Secondhand and came home with the Iron Man. She unwrapped it from the dirty newspaper at tea-time and my father said: 'Where'd ye get that ugly bugger o' a thing?'

29

'Hughie Robertson, don't be vulgar,' she said sternly. 'It's a *bronze*. Old Pillans gave me a bargain. I got it for a shilling.'

'Then old Pillans bought it for half-nothing. He never gave a bargain in his life. What're ye going to do with it?'

Triumphantly, my mother pushed the small metal-cased clock from the centre of the mantelpiece to one side, nearer to the tin tea caddy with the picture of the King and Queen and set the Iron Man bang in the middle. She then looked at the door to the close and I knew that she was thinking that next time Miss Miller came to our door to talk about vulgar surplus-to-requirement aspidistra pots or to complain about the state of the water closet, she would be overcome by the grandeur of the Iron Man on our mantelpiece.

My mother admired the Iron Man daily, every time she dusted him but, away inside my head, I agreed with my father that he was an ugly bugger and very soon I came to half-hate half-fear him. He stood about eighteen inches high and was not a man at all, I discovered later, but a miniature replica of a suit of medieval armour, with a helmet instead of a head, a helmet which had a visor that rose to show the black emptiness inside and fell back with a horrid, little dead 'clonk' when my mother dusted it. In its right hand, which was a scaly iron glove, it held upright an axe with a long handle, the end of which rested beside its iron shoe while the blade rose above its right shoulder. It was the only unfunctional thing in our house that my mother had ever spent money on—the parlour curtains and the aspidistra had their uses—and, perhaps because of this, it had an over-significant dominating quality. With its cold, blind metallic outline, it took on for me the uncanny aspect of a malevolent spirit that presided over our home and it seemed to form a tie, invisible yet real, snaky, sinuous and slimy between our house and old Pillans. Sometimes, at night, when I was in my chairbed, and the light of the candle flickered, the Iron Man *was* old Pillans, leering down at me with terrible cunning from the mantelpiece.

Not long after the Iron Man came to stay, the New Year came in and as a matter of course the upstairs water closet overflowed once more because it could not stomach the extra beer and whisky that came to it in the course of the celebrations, so that it vomited all over the upstairs landing, down the stairs and into the close. Christmas was not celebrated much in the Terrace, especially not in our house. I hung up my stocking, because all children did that and in it in the morning there used to be an apple and an orange which were my fruit supply for the year. The New Year, however, was celebrated by all the men and some of the women getting drunk and this led to the trouble with the upstairs water closet that brought Miss Miller and my mother together in the unity of indignation. In this way, Miss Miller saw the Iron Man, admired it graciously and my mother, even more graciously, said: 'Yes. It's nice, isn't it? A present from my old employers, the Simpsons of Laurelbank. They have a lovely collection of bronzes in their dining-room up there.'

This about the Iron Man being a present was a lie but my mother and Miss Miller often told lies to one another. The only point on which they basically agreed was their own superiority over all the other women in Railway Terrace and Tramway Buildings but they strove continually to establish their superiority over one another. My mother held a very strong card in that she was a married woman while Miss Miller was a spinster but, on Saturday nights when my father got drunk instead of coming home solemn and sober like Miss Miller's brother to conduct prayers in preparation for Sunday, being married was a doubtful asset. Miss Miller held a good card in that her house contained three rooms instead of two, the only other such house in the Terrace being the corner one at the other end and of course Miss Miller's brother was a railway guard while my father was a labourer in the railway siding. Also, Miss Miller played the organ in church, whatever that might mean, for I had never been to church but that it was connected with church made it a good card. On the other side though, Miss Miller had never 'been out and about' as my mother had been when she worked at Laurelbank in Lochview Crescent. Miss Miller had been 'stuck all her days' in The Terrace, looking after her old father and mother until they died, so that Miss Miller did not know what was what, as my mother did. Apart from all this, though, my mother held a secret trump card which held her spirits up in the face of all Miss Miller's uppishness. Through her economy, my mother intended one day to move out of Railway Terrace and up to Victoria Drive, leaving Miss Miller to die in the house where she had been born without having improved her circumstances in any way. My mother's attitude, expressed only in secret glances and narrowings of her eyes, was that Miss Miller might have a good pay coming in now, so that she could be uppish and light a fire in her parlour to sit by on Sundays but the day would come when Miss Miller would see what was what. My mother would move away to Victoria Drive, throw out all the old furniture in our present house and refurnish throughout on the money accumulated through her economy, while Miss Miller, with her brother on a small pension, would have to pull her belt in.

At the dictates of this master plan, therefore, our house was, as my mother described it, 'plain with nothing vulgar.' Her economy was so ingenious, so thorough, so doggedly pursued that it amounted almost to a creative art and she derived from it, I think, a satisfaction similar to that which an artist derives from his activity. She could light a fire with one small piece of wood, although she did this very seldom, the gas ring being more economical for our meagre cooking. She could make a small piece of yellow soap last for three months in spite of all her washing of clothes and scrubbing of floors, for she was fanatically clean and she could make two salt herrings and a few potatoes make a meal for three of us. Admittedly, I was always hungry, seldom felt throughout my entire childhood that I had had enough to eat but, at the same time, I was never ill. I was a small thin child with wispy, slightly curling fair hair and blue eyes and while the school pursued its annual round of chickenpox, measles, mumps, whooping cough, impetigo and the rest, I attended day after day, impervious to infection, wrapped in an inexplicable immunity.

I have often wondered down the years how much of physical disease originates in a mental attitude. Medically, I suppose, the measles infection attacks the physical organism regardless of the mind which that organism contains, but my first attitude to illness was that I did not dare to be ill and cause my mother the expense of medical attention and, later on, having come unscathed through a number of epidemics, I took the attitude that impetigo and the rest attacked other people but not myself.

By implication, my mother contrived to give the impression that to be ill was 'vulgar' and the brown scabs of impetigo were the most vulgar of all ailments. 'Vulgar' was one of my mother's favourite words. To eat too much was vulgar and to buy fish and chips wrapped in newspaper from the Italian shop next door to the church was more vulgar still. To throw pennies out of the window to the old man who played 'Tipperary' on a melodeon was vulgar and to have a halfpenny on Saturday and run to the little shop to buy sweets was especially vulgar. As she often said, my mother knew what was what in this way, with her experience of the refinement of Laurelbank, a house where five were kept and a man and boy in the garden. Our kitchen might be plain, she often said, but it contained nothing vulgar like that uppish Miss Miller's kitchen next door, with its fretwork letter-rack and its painted paper fan on the sideboard. Sideboard, if you please!

My father was not at all like my mother. I did not know him very well, because he was out at work all day, drunk on Saturdays and sleeping it off on Sundays, but he was different from my mother in that he never said that he knew what was what. And, of course, he had no idea of economy, spending all that good money on drink every Saturday night. Seeing very little of my father, I think my impressions of him were gathered largely from my mother and I remember that, although he got drunk on Saturday nights like most of the other men, he was never vulgar in public. He did not get into fights and he did not have to be picked up from the roadside and be dragged home to the close by some of his cronies like Mr. Davidson along at Number Eleven. He was vulgar only in the privacy of our kitchen after he was in bed when, from my chairbed across the room, I would hear my mother say: 'Stop that, you! Keeping *her* in food and you in drink is enough without another mouth in the house!' Then, quite often, there would be a creaking of the bed, a funny sort of laugh from my father and then I would hear my mother getting out of bed altogether as she said: 'Hughie Robertson, go to sleep and stop your vulgarity!'

I did not see a great deal of either of my parents when I think of it, because I preferred to be anywhere, even at school or at Sunday school, rather than in our house. Apart from the presence of the Iron Man, the house was so dimly lit, so harshly clean, so bare and tidy that you could not do anything in it. I went to the house for meals, of course, because I was always hungry but, as soon as the food was inside me, I would be so overcome by a feeling of vulgarity because I had eaten all that food that cost so much money, that I could not get out of the house quickly enough, especially after I had gone to school and had become a full member of the Lochfoot child tribe.

School, which my granny said would stand me in good stead all my life and which my mother said was a waste of time for a girl who would go to domestic service as soon as she was old enough to leave it, led me into a new sin. One day, without knowing how it had happened, I discovered that I could read, that I liked to read, that reading was a sort of miracle by which you could take into your head thoughts and ideas that had been written down by other people. Reading, you could be 'in it' with all sorts of people whom you had never seen and would never see.

Reading was a sin different from all the other sins to which my mother and my teacher said I was so prone, because it was so secret, secret not only from my mother and my teacher, but secret also from all my schoolfellows who, had they known that I liked something that smacked so strongly of the classroom, would have called me a 'softie.'

My mother did not approve of people who 'sat about bookreading' and, although she read the *People's Friend* herself, she read it only on Sunday afternoons and evenings for, although God did not mind women cleaning up the house and cooking the dinner on Sunday forenoons while the men slept it off, God objected to anyone sewing or knitting on Sundays. You could get sent to Hell for doing these things, so on Sundays my mother read the *People's Friend* instead of doing the things that she did on other afternoons and evenings. But I did no reading in the house. I did my reading in the water closet.

This dim little smelly compartment under the stairs borrowed its light from the close through a small pane of frosted glass in its door and the light thus borrowed was very limited but the water closet had a bundle of squares of newspaper hanging, by a string through their corners, from a nail in the wall. Miss Miller provided most of the paper for the water closet. My mother and father did not read newspapers because my mother said what difference did the news make and they were just a waste of good money, so our contribution to the closet consisted of cut-up sugar bags and the like and Miss Miller often complained that our contribution also contributed to blocking up, but then Miss Miller was always complaining about something.

However, living alone with her brother and having no children around her, Miss Miller was rich enough to have not only a Glasgow evening newspaper every day but also the

35

Lochfoot Leader and the *People's Friend* once a week and because of her readable supplies to the water closet and her passing on of the readable *People's Friend* to my mother, I forgave her a great deal and tried not to hang about in the close too much, even when it was raining.

As time went on, my reading developed from a sinful secret pastime into a sinful secret addiction and, as is well known, an addict will go to monstrous lengths to satisfy his craving. Soon the *People's Friend* and the squares of paper in the water closet were not nearly enough and I had no access to any books except my school 'reading book' which the school lent me each year and this I read on the evening of the day I received it. But books could be acquired by various means and smuggled into my secret place behind some loose bricks behind the boiler in the wash-house at the bottom of the yard. They could be read in the wash-house too or conveyed from there, in very cold weather, hidden up the front of my jersey, to the water closet, when I would bolt the door and settle down in the poor light amid the pungent stench that no amount of scrubbing could eradicate.

There was a Village girl whose home seemed to be stuffed with books which she was always willing to lend and books could be 'pinched' from the newspaper shop round the corner which had a Penny Library down at its far end. Old Tommy, who kept this shop, had a peg leg and only one eye which made him easy prey. In addition to newspapers and the Penny Library, he sold tobacco, comic postcards and odds and ends of china while he was also the town's illicit bookmaker, so that he was almost always engaged in secretive transactions at the corner of his counter. On a shelf next to the Penny Library, Tommy had a collection of china which was always of interest to us children and he did not object to our looking at it. This consisted of mustard pots in the form of water closets in white porcelain about three inches high with 'Hot Stuff' written on their lids; chamber pots of similar miniature size which had, written inside them: 'What I see I do not tell so play your part and treat me well,' and a few other similar knick-knacks.

I would go into the shop, pass straight down to the shelf of china and wait for Tommy to become involved in one of his illicit transactions. Then, thin as I was, I could push a book from the Penny Library up under my jersey without looking in any way suspicious or abnormal and, strangely enough, it was always more difficult to return books to the Penny Library than it was to pinch them. A book seemed to come off the shelf and up my jersey in an easy natural way, like the Burn flowing down to the loch but to get a book down from my jersey and back on to the shelf had the difficulty that lies in overcoming some elemental force, such as gravity.

One Saturday morning, I was in the water closet with the book I had pinched from Tommy's the night before and no sooner was I comfortably away on my mental safari than Miss Miller had urgent need of the amenities of my sanctum. So urgent was her need that, when I emerged with my book up my jersey to leave the place free for her, I discovered that she had left the door of her house standing open and unguarded, a thing that had never happened before. Naturally, I popped in to have a look and it was all very uppish and vulgar with a cloth with bobbles on it draped over the mantelpiece, the fretwork letter-rack and the sideboard-if-you-please but in the parlour—this was almost unbelievable—there was a stand of three wooden shelves, all three filled with books. This seemed to me providential for, by this time, I had read almost everything in the Penny Library, everything that Isabel Adair the girl from the Village could lend me and I had been at a loss for another source.

After that, every Saturday forenoon when the coalman came and Miss Miller stood by his cart outside to see that he carried full sacks into her kitchen bunker, I hid in the water closet and nipped into her parlour to pinch a book between two of the coalman's journeys from cart to bunker. Miss Miller was a pest with her need for the water closet every time I was ensconced there but I forgave her much because of her bookshelf, even the doses of castor oil which she caused me to have, castor oil which was horrible to taste and cost a lot of money as well, consequently making you, the unwilling swallower of it, feel not only sick but vulgar. I had the first dose of castor oil on the day that Miss Miller said to my mother: 'That girl is up to no good in there all the time, the dirty little thing.' I was only too well aware that I was up to no good, reading like this and was more than surprised when my mother pulled me into our house, then said: 'I may not have much, Miss Miller but thank God I haven't a vulgar *mind*!' and shut our door in Miss Miller's face. After the door had shut, my mother gave me a shake that nearly brought the book out of my jersey and asked: 'What *were* you doing in that closet?' whereupon I made the standard reply to all adult questions of this nature which was: 'Nothing.' This led my mother to believe that I was constipated, hence the sickly vulgarity of the castor oil but at least it ensured the legitimacy of my several visits to the water closet on the following day, Sunday.

One Saturday forenoon, during the coalman's visit, I had made a successful trip from closet to Miss Miller's parlour, returning one book to the shelves and taking out another on which I had had my eye for some time. It was a large tome called *The Wide Wide World*, a tale which kept me in blissful tears for several weeks, a book which it was a real sacrifice to replace on Miss Miller's shelves long afterwards, but that is by the way. I was doing my reading in the wash-house at this time and I put my book away in the hole in the wall about mid-afternoon and came into the house to see if my mother felt prosperous enough to afford me a slice of bread and jam. Just as I took the first bite, Miss Miller tapped at our door. She then did something that she had never done before. She invited my mother, in a horrified whisper, across the close and into her own house. So far, my mother had had no more than glimpses of the fretwork letter-rack and the sideboard-if-you-please from the open door. This was so strange, this first crossing of Miss Miller's threshold, that I held my breath, clutched my piece of bread and followed. Through the kitchen we went and on into the parlour where, lying on the floor, there was a soiled square of damp paper that had obviously come from the water closet. The two women stood, looking down at it, mystified and as horrified as if it had been a human corpse while I felt panic rise in me like a tide that threatened to bring back the few mouthfuls of bread and jam that I had swallowed. However suspicion, which has the quick sharp head of a snake as well as the implacability of an Iron Man, did not turn towards me. *The Wide Wide World* was safely hidden in the wash-house and this piece of paper, carried in on the sole of my black, laced winter boot, was on the carpet but the snake-like head did not turn my way.

'Somebody's been in here, in my very parlour, Mrs. Robertson,' Miss Miller said, but not accusingly. The words were more of an appeal for sympathy and understanding and my mother responded in the manner required.

'*That* came from the water closet,' she said. 'Is that not terrible? Is anything missing, Miss Miller?'

'No, thank goodness.' Miss Miller indicated a table by the wall which held a teapot and a biscuit barrel which I thought were made of shiny tin and two ornaments which were sprays of iron flowers. 'All the valuables are still there,' she said.

They went on speculating for a long time while Miss Miller checked the contents of a cupboard and two drawers and looked inside the upright piano but she did not examine the bookcase or, indeed, pay the slightest attention to it. Books, it seemed, were so valueless that nobody would steal them. I had known already that to read books was sinful and I now learned that books were valueless as well but, if these things were so, why did Miss Miller have books in her parlour at all? It was very puzzling.

At long last, Miss Miller said: 'I feel quite faint, really I do. Such a terrible thing!' She looked down at the square of newspaper which lay there on the carpet, not knowing its own importance, unconscious of being part of this drama, unaware of being 'in it' with us all. 'Mrs. Robertson, will you take a cup o' tea?' she continued. 'I'll put the kettle on. Would you be good enough to take the coal tongs and put *that* on the fire for me?'

'I will indeed,' said my mother co-operatively and added, in a different tone, to myself: 'Don't make crumbs on Miss Miller's carpet. Go outside and play.'

Outside, the sleet was blowing in drifts across the backyard so I retired to the wash-house but, before returning to *The Wide Wide World*, I contemplated my misfortune in being a child, a member of a genus that Miss Miller did not like, for I was sure that her uppishness was greater than her economy and that my mother was probably, at this very moment, being offered biscuits or perhaps even cake, having washed her hands ostentatiously at Miss Miller's sink after having, with the tongs, put *that* into the fire.

It was some weeks before this contretemps in Miss Miller's parlour showed its beneficent effect but the effect came, having followed a devious sinuous route from its cause in the mysterious way of the world.

My mother, for the first time, had penetrated not only across Miss Miller's threshold but into her parlour and in the parlour she had seen the bookshelves with the books and that evening, while my father was out getting drunk, I was inspired to say: 'Ma, isn't Miss Miller's parlour lovely?' I had already learned to amuse myself by irritating my mother in innocent-seeming ways.

'So-so,' she said, frowning over her darning.

'Did you see the piano and the books and everything?'

'Pianos!' my mother snorted out derisively. 'And not much of a bookcase either. For a bookcase, you should see the one in the drawing-room at Laurelbank, glass doors and everything and if there's one book in it, there's three hundred.'

For days I dreamed of the magnificence of a house that contained three hundred books but the dreams gave way to rapture when I came home one evening to go to bed and found on the wall, above my chairbed, a case of three shelves about three feet long, enclosed by glass doors and all three shelves packed with books. My mother had been down to the Secondhand again and had acquired all this for half-a-crown. That it had come from Pillans's was its one flaw in my eyes, for this meant that his slimy-looking hands might have touched it but my mother, of course, had cleaned it. The woodwork was polished, the glass shone and the brass knobs of the doors sparkled so that the trail of snail's slime which, I was sure, was always left by the hands of Pillans had been removed. As for the books inside, I was certain that he had never touched them at all, books being valueless.

My mother was almost smiling over her bargain, not because she intended to read the second-rate novels and the volumes of sermons that the case contained but because she had acquired something that was neither uppish nor vulgar and which put our kitchen 'upsides' with Miss Miller's parlour. And my mother was gratified by my rapturous and genuine admiration but her demeanour changed when I jumped on to my chairbed and reached a hand towards the brass knobs.

'Don't you touch that!' she said sharply. 'I didn't pay good money for that for *you* to make a mess of it. If you lay a hand on that bookcase, you'll suffer for it!'

I jumped down on to the floor but already I knew how to read these books in secret. I still had Miss Miller's brown-covered *The Wide Wide World* in the wash-house and it could replace the books I would pinch from the case. Miss Miller would never miss it and my mother would never notice a stranger in her fold. It was strange that when you were 'in it' with a thing as I was in it with books you knew exactly how other people who were not in it with them felt about them.

That night the bookcase came, I lay on my back in my chairbed and looked up at the wall behind my head. I had never done this since the Iron Man came but now I looked up at the polished underside of the bookcase. Alongside the case, on the end of the mantelpiece, was fixed the curly iron bracket of the gas-light but this never burned because my mother's economy dictated that candles were cheaper. A candle was burning now, in its flat enamel holder on the red-covered kist beside her chair. Her back was towards me, her shoulders hunched, her head bent as she sewed an old piece of tweed into a skirt for myself and she looked like the picture in the Salvation Army leaflet about the woman who worked so hard that she died because her husband spent all their money on drink. When I thought of it, my father was round at the pub this very minute and yet life in my home was not like the Salvation Army leaflet said. My father did not hit my mother and me, no matter how drunk he was and he did not swear and blaspheme. In truth, it was my mother who did these things really in spite of the fact that she did not speak a word or move a muscle when my father came home drunk. She did not strike him nor did she use bad language because to do such things would be vulgar, but she looked at him and kept silent in a way that was much worse than swearing at him or striking him.

While I had been thinking these thoughts, I had stopped seeing the hunched figure of my mother, the candle flame and the other features of our kitchen because my eyes had been turned inwards towards the thoughts inside my head, but now I began to look out again and upwards to the underside of the bookcase, this most desirable new circumstance in my life. Using this word inside my mind, the longest word I knew, it struck me that all your circumstances went on making more circumstances, that everything was so inter-connected in such a web that you could never disentangle it.

At Bible, we were told that God sent all the good things and that the Devil sent all the bad things but the books, which I was certain were good things, had not been sent by either God or the Devil, but had arrived in our kitchen because my mother wanted to be upsides with Miss Miller. Then, my mother had only come to know about Miss Miller's bookcase because I had tramped a bit of water closet paper on to Miss Miller's carpet.

Staring at the wall above my head where the candle flame was throwing the snake-like shadow of the gas bracket on the wall, I noticed that this shadow made a dim, sinuous connecting link between the bookcase and the Iron Man on the mantelpiece, the good thing and the bad thing between which I had thought it impossible for there to be any connection, even the most shadowy. But there were connections everywhere, between all the circumstances so that, indeed, my circumstances were simply a long, snaky twisted chain of connections, one circumstance growing out of another and another out of another and yet another out of—

The longer I contemplated the long snake in my mind, the more frightening it became, for I saw that I had no more control over this tortuous chain than I had over the shadow of the gas bracket on the wall. The pointed jet of the bracket in shadow looked like the head of a little snake that wavered, twisting this way and that, as if searching for something, reaching out for another circumstance to connect and add to the web, with every flicker of the candle flame. I had not meant to carry that square of paper on to Miss Miller's carpet. Had I known it was sticking to my boot I would have pulled it off. I had been wicked in going into Miss Miller's parlour to pinch a book but out of that wickedness had come this bookcase above my head. It seemed that what I did was immaterial, that the snake would move on, making connection after connection, as it coiled on its mysterious way, weaving hither and yon like the blindly searching little shadow on the wall.

Suddenly, my mother laid her sewing aside and blew out the candle. Bookcase, gas bracket and Iron Man all disappeared into the darkness. All the circumstances and all the connections disappeared from sight but they were still there, still in control. Very frightened, I reached out silently with my mind through the dark to my mother. Partly from economy, partly from what she called 'modesty', she always undressed in the dark but I knew all the stages of the process from secret observation during the long light summer evenings. It was comforting now to hear the clicking as the steel hooks of her stays were released, the faint peeling noise as she took off her long black woollen stockings. This had the comfort of familiarity, making the deeper more frightening thoughts sink into the muzziness deep inside my head and as I felt sleep coming, I began to repeat, silently, my verse of the hymn that would earn me the strap the next morning if I did not know it.

> *There's a home for little children*
> *Above the bright blue sky,*
> *Where Jesus reigns in glory,*
> *A home of peace and joy.*
> *No home on earth is like it*
> *Or can with it compare,*
> *For everyone is happy,*
> *Nor could be happier there.*

It sounded like a place where there were no circumstances.

CHAPTER THREE

Loving Shepherd of Thy sheep
Keep me Lord, in safety keep;
Nothing can Thy power withstand,
None can pluck me from Thy hand.

HYMN 668

IN THE DAYTIME of course, when I was out of doors and among my fellows, I did not believe in all that stuff about a home above the bright blue sky. These hymns were just a lot of rubbish that you had to learn at school to avoid getting the strap and the only homes there were for children were Number Three Railway Terrace and several hundred like it, unless you were Castle folk and could live in the Village or so rich that you could live up Lochview. After I had been at school for a year, I became very conscious of my connection with Castle folk and the Village, tenuous as that connection was and often there was a wavering in my mind like the frail movement of the shadow of the gas bracket on the wall. The basic law of the child tribe of the Terrace and the Buildings was conformity. The clothing—tweed skirts and jerseys for the girls, tweed shorts and jerseys for the boys—was uniform and any poor wretch who was sent to school in clothing that differed from this standard was the butt of all the others. It was protocol to scorn school, parents and every form of authority and any child who contributed to his or her home life by helping in the house or fetching groceries from the shop did so to loud shouts of 'Mammy's big softie' from the others. For most of the time, I found it desirable to conform, to be an unquestioning and unquestioned member of the tribe but, occasionally, I would find myself withdrawing from the group and the current game, scampering round a corner and before I had fully realized

45

it, I would be running down the curve of road under the Castle wall that led to the Village and Lilac Cottage. The journey down the road was short but to make it was to move from one world into another, as if one had moved along the shadow of the gas bracket from the world of the Iron Man to the world of the bookcase.

Like Lochview Crescent, the Village had a separate identity but an identity different from that of the Crescent. There was no withdrawn drawn-blinds silence in the Village. The windows of the cottages were as alive as bright eyes and there were always people pottering about in their little front gardens or chatting to one another over the low flower-decked walls that separated them. And Railie and Trammie children never went raiding down the Village as they went raiding up Lochview. It may have been that we were afraid of being confronted by the faction of Village children if we did so, for they would probably have put us to inglorious rout, but I did not think that this was the sole reason why the Village was immune to our depredations. It had a kindly welcoming decorum, with this open-ness, its lack of high walls and iron railings and to Railies and Trammies it was a place for a quiet walk on Sundays, when you came home in a roundabout way from Sunday school, wearing your Sunday clothes and buttoned boots. As you came along the road, people taking the sun in their front gardens would speak to you. 'Fine day. Been to the Sunday school?' they would say and not: 'Here you, get away out of it' which was the prevailing greeting given to us around the Terrace, the Buildings or the streets of the town. There was even one old man in the Village who had an apple tree growing on the wall of his house and when you came past in September, on the Sunday that Sunday school started for the winter, he would pick the apples off and hand one to each child over the wall. We Railies and Trammies were expert fruit-pinchers. We invariably pinched all the apples, plums and pears from the gardens up Lochview in spite of old Beery-belly's best efforts to stop us, but although this old man's apples were much bigger and sweeter, we did not ever make a raid on his garden.

All that you could say was that the Village was 'different' just as, in the school playground, the Villagers themselves were different. When we went raiding up Lochview or down to the station or to the tramway depot to have a lark with old Loco or old Squeak, the Tinker faction would join us sometimes but the Villagers never did. They were an integral part of the playground, participating in all the games but once outside the iron gates, the Villagers separated from the rest of the tribe and turned down the curve of road towards their homes.

Each faction in the playground had a leader, of course— two leaders, really, a boy and a girl but the boy was the leader-in-chief, except in the case of the Village faction which was always dominated by Isabel Adair, although she was only two years older than myself. Also, since the Village tended to dominate all the other factions, this meant that Isabel dominated the entire playground.

The Villagers were fewer in number than the other factions but, in a way mysterious to me, they had what I vaguely recognized as quality on their side so that they could always overthrow mere quantity. Isabel was about twice my physical size and weight, with long shining dark brown curls bunched together into a red ribbon bow at the nape of her neck and hanging down her back like a mane. She was beautifully proportioned, with long shapely legs on which she strode about the playground like some miniature Boadicea and she was absolutely fearless. She could fight with her fists as well as any boy but she could also claw and bite like a girl and not even the biggest of the Railie, Trammie or Tinker boys would join issue with Isabel single-handed while, if two or three of them set upon her, there were her three brothers, David, Colin and Ian to reckon with. The brothers were all younger than Isabel but, like her, they were well-grown and Ian, the six-

47

year-old, was a fit adversary for any Railie, Trammie or Tinker.

Isabel's home in the Village was Holly Cottage, next door to my granny's house but I had been admiring Isabel in the school playground for a long time before I knew this. I discovered it one Saturday morning when I suddenly withdrew from a game among the forest of clothes-poles in the backyard and ran down the road to the Village. When I came to the first cottage, I stopped running, of course, and began to skip instead, right along the middle of the road because there was no traffic in the Village except maybe the baker's old horse ambling along from door to door. Skipping, I began to understand why I had come to the Village this morning.

My father had come home drunk the night before. He was getting drunk more often nowadays and not only on Saturday nights. He was not very drunk but he had been spending money in the pub and my mother was angry about that and, as she always did when she was angry, she began to say things about my granny and Lilac Cottage. This was a very queer thing, that no matter what my mother first started being angry about, she always ended by being angry about my granny and Lilac Cottage and yet I could understand it a little bit. My mother wanted more than anything to be rich and have a nice house and be in good circumstances and she felt that a nice house like Lilac Cottage was wasted on my granny who did not want to be upsides with Miss Miller or improve her circumstances in any way. My granny was quite happy as she was and this made my mother angry.

When my mother said things about my granny like the things she had said the night before, I always felt uneasy, in case the things could travel through the air, invisibly, from Railway Terrace to the Village and do my granny some harm so I was really going down to Lilac Cottage to make sure that she was all right. And so she was. She was sitting in her chair beside her fire which burned all the year round, knitting a sock.

'So there you are, Jean!' she greeted me. 'Well, you've caught me! Here I am sitting on my backside knitting in the middle o' the forenoon. I havena even swept the floor the-day.'

It was queer. It was as if some of the things my mother had said the night before really had travelled down here, things like '*Her*, living in that good house and she'll hardly even bother to sweep the floor!' But although the things seemed to have travelled, they had done my granny no harm and she continued: 'But first things first, Jean. These socks are for Willie the Carter's birthday and that's the morn. Jamieson the Draper took so long to get the wool I wanted. Willie is very good about sawing sticks for me and I aye do him a pair o' socks for his birthday an' a pair for the New Year. Well, how are you the-day?'

'I'm fine, Granny. I'll sweep the floor,' I said and while she went on with her knitting, I set about the task with pleasure. When I had finished the sweeping and dusting, I went out to the shed at the back to bring in enough firewood to last her over Sunday. I do not think I performed these small services out of any thought for or duty to my granny. Doing these things was a form of playing house in a real house. It was against the law of the child tribe to help in the home but this was because most mothers wanted their children to help. In my home, it was different. I was never allowed to do any household tasks at home because my mother said that I would not do them properly because I was a useless wee thing who did not know what was what and that I would bump the broom against the skirting board and spoil the varnish. But my granny seemed to enjoy having little things done for her, always seemed pleased with the way I did them and it was pleasant to bring in armfuls of sweet-smelling logs and stack them neatly in the corner by the hearth. When I had brought in all that the log-corner would hold, I went out to have a look at the back garden, for my granny was not a talkative woman in an out-loud way but even out in the garden I could feel her contentedly knitting by her fire and sending some of her contentment out to me to wrap me around like a warm shawl.

On the other side of the garden wall this morning, there was a large fat woman with a smiling face, the kind of face that you did not see in Railway Terrace, who was brushing with a hand brush rugs which were draped on the wall.

'Well,' she said, as these Village people did, as if she were really pleased to see me, 'so you are down to see your granny?'

'Yes,' I said, uncomfortable as I always was because I had no standard response for these people who were pleased to see me.

If she had frowned and said: 'What are *you* doing here?' it would have been simple, for one would merely say: 'Mind your own business, you old bizzom,' stick out one's tongue and run away. However, there she was, smiling over the wall. 'And how is your granny the-day?' she asked.

'She's fine,' I said and then added, 'thank you.'

'And what is your name? You are Hugh Robertson's lassie, aren't you?'

Isabel Adair's pink-cheeked face now appeared over the wall and said: 'That's wee Jeanie Robertson, Ma. She's in Colin's class at the school.'

'You go in and put the kettle on. We can manage without your help,' said Mrs. Adair, but good-naturedly and Isabel went to do her bidding at once, while I tried to imagine what would happen in the school playground if anybody tried to send Isabel about her business like this.

'What's your name, pet?' Mrs. Adair asked me again as if Isabel had never interrupted us.

'Jean,' I said. 'Jean Robertson.'

'And a fine name too.'

'Could I help you with the rugs?' I asked. 'Could I brush the bits on this side of the wall?'

'Aye, if you like. Here you are,' Mrs. Adair said and handed the little brush over to my side.

As I finished brushing the rugs, she carried them one by one into the house until with the last one in a roll under her arm, she said: 'You'd better jump over and come in and get a piece after all that hard work.'

I was under instruction from my mother never to accept 'pieces' from anybody, especially the mothers of other children, because my own mother's economy dictated her non-intention of giving pieces in return to anybody, but this was an instruction that I never obeyed. Always hungry, I accepted any piece that was offered to me. The offers around Railway Terrace and Tramway Buildings were very few but sometimes the man at the Co-op would send me to the station on an errand and give me some broken biscuits when I came back. I now hopped smartly over the wall between my granny's garden and that of Holly Cottage and followed Mrs. Adair in through her back door to her big kitchen.

This was the most cheerful place I had ever seen. It had a window at each end, one looking to the back and one to the road out in front and on each windowsill there sat a bright red geranium, thriving in its brown earthenware pot and bearing a curious, cheerful healthy resemblance to Mrs. Adair herself. Like her flowers, she seemed to bloom with colour and brim with life. I snatched a quick glance at the mantel above the bright fire. There was no Iron Man but it held a wooden-cased clock, two brass candlesticks, two china dogs with gold collars round their necks, two brass tea caddies and two brass trays standing upright against the wall like round golden suns. Was it vulgar? I was not sure, but I liked it because it was so sparkling and gay. Even if it is vulgar, I thought to myself daringly, I like it.

At a table in the middle of the floor, Mrs. Adair was splitting enormous floury scones and slapping on to them great heaped spoonfuls of rhubarb jam which she spread out over them in a lavish bounteous way with the back of the spoon. She then cut a piece off the corner of one and gave it to a little boy of about two years old who was sitting on the floor playing with some little red bricks and then she picked up one of the huge, inch-thick floury triangles and handed it, all of it and bursting with jam, to me. Never in my life before had I had so much food in my hands at one time.

I began to go to the Village every Saturday forenoon now, did some jobs for my granny and was invariably called over the wall to the Adair kitchen to have scones and jam at eleven o'clock, after which I would stay to play with Isabel and her brothers and some of the other Village children until dinner-time. They played all sorts of exciting games from Hide and Seek to Cowboys and Indians, just as we did up at the Terrace but they had wonderful places to hide and a wide territory over which to gallop their imaginary horses, for at the bottom of the back gardens, extending the length of the Village, there was a long strip of grass, dotted with clumps of gorse and no matter where you looked there was not a single iron clothes-pole, high brick wall or row of railings.

After an energetic game in which we girls, led by Isabel, had won the Battle of Bannockburn against the boys led by her oldest brother, she and I were sitting by a gorse bush with our backs to the houses of the Village. We looked across a low wall that had ferns growing out of it to a wide rolling green space, again dotted with clumps of gorse and also with grey sheep and young woolly white lambs. Beyond this, far away, there was a group of buildings backed by woods and beyond them, further away still, green hills rose gently to the pale blue of the early summer sky.

'This is a great place for playing,' I ventured to say, in an attempt to show my gratitude for this splendid morning. 'It's great—honest.'

'It's too wee just now for a right set-to,' said Isabel, 'but it'll be back to normal next week when my Dad gets these ewes and

lambs away up to the hill and we get the Home Park back.'
With this, she waved a careless, shapely sun-tanned hand
at the huge expanse where the sheep were. 'It's the same every
year,' she said. 'We have to give up the Home Park for the
lambing.'

At this moment, there came a cry from a boy. 'Here, you
Adairs! Here's your Dad for the ewes. We'll get the Park back!'

'We'll get the Park back!' everybody shouted and shouting
with the rest, I ran with them and sat as they did on the wall
among the ferns while a big man with a tall stick and two
dogs came walking across the field among the sheep. As he
came nearer, he grew bigger and bigger, far bigger than old
Beery-belly, even, bigger than any man I had ever seen. I
climbed down from the wall on to the ground behind.

'That your dad?' I asked Isabel, my eyes on the tall broad
figure.

'Aye.' I began to move away. 'Where you going?' she
asked.

'I'd better get home.'

'What for? You should stop and watch the sheep getting
gathered.'

I suddenly understood that this Village tribe of children had
its tribal customs too, just as we of the Railie and Trammie
tribes did. There were, throughout the year, certain happenings that Railies and Trammies always attended, such as going
down to the police station on Hogmanay to see Beery-belly
bringing in the worst of the fighting drunks and going to the
church door on a certain Sunday to jeer at the Free Masons
going to their special service, with their solemn faces and their
funny little aprons worn in front of their trousers. This gathering of the sheep, I now understood, was one of the happenings
of the Village tribe's year and I was being invited to be 'in it',
in spite of being a Railie of very slight connection with the
Village.

Suddenly the big man gave a long shrill whistle and waved

53

his long stick and the two dogs went racing wide round the field until they had gathered all the sheep and lambs into a tight woolly mass which began to move away from us towards the gate on the other side of the field where the man had come in. Suddenly, though, there was a short low whistle and all the sheep stopped moving while one dog lay down behind and the other in front. The man then moved right in among this mass of savage horned animals, pushing them aside, but gently, with his legs and his stick until he bent down and picked up a little white lamb, looking at its front leg before tucking it under his arm.

'A lame one,' said Isabel. 'Shame. Poor wee thing!'

There was now another whistle and as the sheep began to move again, the man let them flow away in front of him as he turned towards us and waved his stick. Isabel jumped down from the ferny wall into the sheep field, the whole row of children jumped down, so I jumped down too and ran with them until we had caught up with the man, forming a flock of children instead of sheep around him. He smiled at us, as if he were pleased to see us all and the lamb under his arm said 'Baa!' while its mother walked trustingly along, rubbing her wool against the man's leg. Close to, he was gigantic. My head was barely level with the pocket of his coat and we all had to run to keep up with his long strides. He did not seem to me to be like anybody's father. He did not look like a real man at all but more like the giant in a fairy story or somebody far away and not quite real like the men in the Old Testament part of the Bible. I was afraid of him and wanted to run away back to the Terrace but I was hemmed in by Isabel and the others and had to keep on running towards the gate.

When we reached it, all the sheep and lambs went pouring through, the man who, I was being forced to believe, was the Adairs' father went through too and then all of us pushed the gate shut from inside the field, so that we were on one side and the big man surrounded by his sheep and with his lamb under

54

his arm, was on the other. He now looked down and round at us all.

'All right,' he said, 'you've got the Home Park back. Rea-eady!'

Isabel pushed me in behind herself and all the other girls made a long line behind us while all the boys made a similar long line behind Isabel's biggest brother, but facing the opposite way.

'Beat the bounds!' the man shouted. 'Go!'

We all began to run, the girls going one way, the boys the other, right round the big field until we all fetched up, girls and boys from opposite directions, at the gate again. Then the man took off his battered old hat, waved it and shouted 'Hip, hip—' and we all shouted a loud 'Hurray!' before he whistled to the dogs and set off along the lane behind his sheep, with the lame lamb still under his arm.

We were all puffing and blowing, for it had been a long run, but my shortness of breath was not only from the running but from the strange splendour of it all, the radiance of running round that field in the sunshine while the big man stood at the gate, watching us and smiling. It was so strange to be doing something that you liked to do and to be sure at the same time that the thing you were doing was not a sin. It was like sweeping the floor for my granny, but much much bigger and grander.

Bemused by the splendid strangeness, I lost all count of time, place and governing things and went on playing in the big field until Isabel said: 'Come on!' and without question, I followed her. Before I realized what was happening, I was back in the big kitchen with the geraniums and Mrs. Adair was saying: 'So you got the Home Park back?' Before any of us could answer, the man—*Mr. Adair*, I told myself sternly inside my head—came in through a door, drying his hands on a striped towel and then he threw the towel aside and picked up the littlest boy from the floor. He tossed the baby up to the ceiling and swung him round and round, then set him down and pretended to box with all three bigger boys at once, prodding a stomach here and slapping a behind there while he danced, laughing, round the room. I had never seen a grown-up person behave like this and stood in a corner by the dresser, staring, until one of the boys, trying to dodge his father, bumped into me and nearly knocked me down.

'Hello,' said Mr. Adair, noticing me for the first time, 'and who is this bonnie wee one?'

'That's Jean—Jean Robertson,' Mrs. Adair told him. 'She came down to see her granny next door and she's been playing.'

'Then she'll be ready for her dinner,' Mr. Adair said. 'Come, Jean,' and he put his big hands round my waist, picked me up and sat me down in a chair next to his own at the table.

Before I could dwell upon the pleasure of being picked up in that comfortable secure way, I was overcome by the sight of the table top. I had never seen so much food. There was soup, thick and luscious with vegetables, followed by a huge lump of beef that had been boiled in the soup and with this we ate cabbage and potatoes and after that we had large platefuls of milk pudding with stewed rhubarb. And then Mrs. Adair, brown teapot in hand, said: 'Will you take a drop o' tea and a scone, Jean?' but, for the first time in my life I had had enough to eat and I felt blissfully unvulgar as I said politely: 'No, thank you, Mrs. Adair.'

When the meal was over, Isabel and the boys and I washed and dried the dishes in the scullery off the kitchen and when we had finished, Mrs. Adair told us to go out and play again. She sat by the fire with the littlest boy in her lap and Mr. Adair was standing beside her, his old hat in one hand, his stick in the other, ready to go back to his sheep. I wanted to make them know what a wonderful day this had been for me, with the run round the big Park and the splendid dinner afterwards but there were no words for this. I could speak only in the standard formulae of the backyards and the playground and there was no formula for dealing with what had happened to me on this day. Still, I was determined to try to convey something, something that would be between this man, woman and me, something that would let them know that I was grateful for being allowed to be so 'in it' with them and their children. I went to stand in front of Mr. Adair, looking up at the great broad height of him.

'Will the wee lamb that has a sore leg be all right, Mr. Adair?' I asked.

Looking down at me, he moved his hat from his right hand to his left hand that held the stick, then put his right hand on my head. The big palm covered my whole head and as it rested gently there I tried to describe inside my head how it felt. The word came into my mind. It felt like a blessing. He smiled down at me.

'Yes, Jean,' he said, 'the wee lamb will be all right,' and I had a great gush of inner satisfaction, a certainty that this smiling man and woman knew what I had meant to convey.

That was my first and my last meal at Holly Cottage. There were shadows on the grass when Mrs. Adair came out to the back garden and called to her own children and to me.

'You must run up home now, Jean,' she said. 'Your mother must be wondering where you are.'

That showed how different Mrs. Adair was, I thought, that she could think that my mother would wonder about me but the thought was a mere glance at the edge of my mind. I was still lost in the splendour of the day, still full of dinner, scones and jam at mid-afternoon and borne on the wings of the freedom on the sunlit grass. Still in a trance, I set off obediently for Railway Terrace and when I went into the house, my mother said sharply:

'And where have *you* been all day?'

Even the sharpness of her voice and glance did not disperse the warm cloud that contained me and out of it, remembering,

I said: 'Down at the Adairs in the Village. We had dinner. There was soup and meat and pudding with——'

My mother sprang up and struck me on the side of the head so that I lost my balance and fell into the chair that was my bed at night. Cowering there, I came back to reality while my mother raged and slapped at me.

'You vulgar brat!' she stormed. 'How often have I told you you are not to go into other people's houses? If you ever go begging dinners from folk again, I'll skin you alive!'

She said a great deal more but, crying, I did not hear. Besides, I was sure that I had heard already many times all that she was saying.

I wished, though, that my mother could be other than she was, that I could make her understand that the Adairs were not as she thought, but I knew that this was not possible. She was angry with me because she was afraid, really, that the Adair family would arrive at the Terrace and expect her to give them a dinner that would cost a lot of money in return for the dinner they had given me. She did not want to give them the dinner but if she did not, she would be what she called 'beholden' to them and she did not like this either. My mother, herself, never gave anything to anybody without expecting even more in return and she thought, naturally, that all people were like herself. Unlike myself, I was sure, she had never been invited to be 'in it' with people as I had been with the Villagers when they got the Home Park back and she had never been invited to have dinner in a kitchen with red geraniums by people who simply enjoyed giving dinner to other people, so it was not possible for my mother to be other than she was.

I was not frightened by her threat to skin me alive because I did not believe that she would do it or do any of the other dreadful things that she threatened. She did not slap me or thrash me as much as most parents in Railway Terrace slapped and thrashed their children and this slapping today was my own stupid fault. After all, I was publicly recognized as the most convincing liar in my class at school and in spite of knowing my mother so well, I had come home and blurted out about the Adairs like some silly little fool in the Baby Class.

It was not because of my mother that I did not have another dinner at the Adairs but because of something my granny told me the following Saturday when, disobedient again, I went down to the Village.

'You had your dinner next door last week, Jean?' she asked.

'Yes, Granny.'

'Don't do that again, lassie.'

'But Mr. Adair asked me, Granny.' Surely, picking you up and setting you in a chair at the table was the same as asking you to dinner? I did not tell lies to my granny.

'Mr. Adair and Mrs. Adair too would give dinner to all Lochfoot if need be but they have a big family of their own and they need all the dinners they've got. If you are down here playing, you can get dinner with me.'

'I'm supposed to go home for my dinner anyway,' I said.

If my mother found out that I was having dinner with my granny, she would be even angrier than she had been about dinner at the Adairs, because it would make her what she called 'beholden to that old bizzom'.

Although my mother had been so very angry with me over that dinner at the Adairs, she was avidly interested in it and in everything I could tell her about the Adair home. Again and again, she had me tell her about the dinner and always she would make some comment like: 'They're lucky to be able to afford it. But soup *and* meat? There's no need for that in a working folk's house. Vulgar, I call it.' And when I had described the Adair mantelpiece to her for perhaps the tenth time, she said as she had said at every other description: 'I don't like brass. It's vulgar and cheap-looking,' and she would look up with satisfaction at the Iron Man.

Although I never had another dinner at the Adairs, I

risked my mother's wrath by eating many a scone and jam there at mid-forenoon on Saturdays because my granny would call the Adairs and me to her back door to get more scones and jam in the afternoon, but my mother never knew of this although she knew now that I went to play in the Village quite frequently.

One evening, when I was in my chairbed and my father, for once, probably because he had no money left for the pub, was sitting opposite my mother beside the empty fireplace, my mother spoke. I had been almost asleep but this was so unusual that it roused me. They seldom spoke to one another, probably because there was nothing to say.

'*She* is not long home,' my mother said. She seldom used my name. She addressed me as 'you' and spoke of me as 'she', with some emphasis on the pronoun as a rule, a habit which had the curious effect of setting me away and apart from herself, as if she were viewing me impersonally and from a distance. 'She went away down to the Village after her tea to play with these Adairs again. Who are they?'

'What?'

My father was taken unawares. He was not accustomed to being spoken to by my mother and on the few occasions when she did address him, his first response was always this word 'what?' He seemed to live away inside himself except when he was drunk and I often wondered what went on inside his head.

'The Adairs,' said my mother, 'in the Village. They live next-door to your stepmother, she tells me.'

'What about them?'

'They seem to be very well-t'-do from what *she* tells me. What's his work?'

'Surely ye know that?' my father asked. 'You lived next-door to them yourself for a while.'

'I keep myself *to* myself.'

'Adair is the Castle shepherd,' my father said in a quiet

60

voice as if he were thinking of something long ago and far away. 'Adairs have been shepherds to the Castle for generations. They're fine folk.'

'Aye, I'm sure o' that, seeing they're Villagers,' my mother said in a nasty voice but my father took no notice of the nastiness. He merely retired inside his own head once more.

So Mr. Adair was a shepherd! *That* is what a shepherd really was, a big man with a smiling face, who looked after sheep and picked up lambs with sore legs? And that was what this latest hymn we were having to learn at Bible was about. It meant that God was a big man like Mr. Adair, even bigger, because all of us Railies and Trammies and Villagers and Tinkers were his sheep and he had to be big enough to keep us all in safety. Inside my head now, I had a clear picture of God, very big, smiling, wearing an old hat which he took off sometimes to shout: 'Hip, hip, hurrah,' and there was always a lamb with a sore leg tucked under his arm.

My days of play in the Home Park behind the Village lasted for less than a summer. The end came one day when the boys had gone off on their own and we girls were picking sides for a game of Rounders. Isabel was captain of one side and a girl called Violet Bryson, whose father was a gardener at the Castle, was captain of the other. Isabel won the toss, which gave her first pick of the players and she picked me because I was a good Rounders player. I had not a hard stroke and could not send the ball very far, but I was small and quick, difficult to hit with the ball when I was on the run between bases and Rounders captains always like to have me on their sides. Violet Bryson became angry.

'*She*'s not in it!' she said. 'I'm sick o' Railies an' I'm not playing with them!'

The word was out. It had been whispering furtively for some time but now it was spoken in a loud spiteful voice and hostility was writhing among us like a snake.

'Railie, dirty Railie!' came a taunting voice and Isabel,

after a startled moment, squared up to fight. She would win the fight, I knew, because she always did. Inside a second she would have a death-grip on the wiry red hair of Violet Bryson and have her screaming for mercy but it would be of no use. They were Villagers and I was a Railie and the fight would only make things worse in the end.

'And I'm not playing with a lot o' cow-dung Villagers!' I shouted into the angry silence. 'Shove your Rounders up your arses,' I added and marched away across the Park, climbed the ferny wall and went away up through my granny's back garden.

After that, I played with the Villagers in their big Home Park no more, but Isabel did not abandon me entirely. In the playground at school, she elected herself my champion and a redoubtable champion she was. Undersized as I was, I was a natural target for bullying and but for Isabel my life would have been a misery but very soon the entire playground knew that to lay a hand on me would bring down the dark-maned avenging fury. Whatever the reason for this protection was, Isabel treated me with a gruff, off-hand yet kindly impatience, as if I were a small feeble-minded sister with whom life had saddled her and in return I looked up to her with gratitude and adoration. In my eyes, Isabel's head with its tousled shining mane of curls was always surrounded by a nimbus of light, a light of the sort which, we were told at Bible, surrounded the throne of God. Indeed, something of this light surrounded the entire Adair home and family in my mind. It came in as sunshine through the two windows of their kitchen across the red geraniums and struck the brass on the mantel to be transmuted into a warm golden glow and through this glow was interwoven the words and music of the hymn 'Loving Shepherd of Thy Sheep'.

But nothing remained except the memory. My mother had plucked me from the hands of Mr. Adair the shepherd and I never saw him again for, during all the hours that I played with his children, he was out at the farm, tending his sheep. And, in time, Isabel drifted away from me too. Like most of the Villagers, Isabel was clever at school. Many of the books that she had lent me had labels on their fly-leaves that said 'Isabel M. Adair. First Prize. Class III' or 'David S. Adair. First Prize. Class II' and of course Colin, the brother who was my age, was always top of my class. And so the day came when Isabel was twelve years old and did not come back to our school. If I went early and the long way round to school, making a loop round the edge of the town and through the Village, I might be lucky enough to meet her, tall and free-striding, her mane of hair tied with a navy blue ribbon now to match her smart new uniform, on her way to catch the tramcar that would take her to the Academy Down-the-line. She would bid me a gay 'Hello, Jeanie' and I would make a timid response and continue on my way to Lochfoot School, feeling small and bereft. After a few weeks, I stopped going the long way round through the Village and nowadays, when I went down on Saturdays to see my granny, Isabel was never at home. She was away playing hockey, already in her first year at the Academy a member of its First Eleven.

But I still had the occupations natural to Railies and Trammies ever since Railway Terrace and Tramway Buildings blotted out the green field of my granny's memory. We still shouted after authority in the streets, we still made raids up Lochview and we still threw stones, fought and stole school chalk to write things on walls and for most of the time I was completely involved in and content with this, my fore-ordained way of life.

After my one visit to the Adair home, however, I looked upon my own home no longer with the eyes of acceptance but with the eyes of enquiry and from observation and stray remarks dropped by my granny, I began to understand a little about my mother and father. Once upon a time, it seemed, they had chosen to marry and live together. This matter of

63

choice was something that had never occurred to me before. All households, with a few exceptions like the Millers' household next door, were made up of mothers, fathers and children and I had thought that this was a natural law, such as the law that ordained the sequence of spring, summer, autumn and winter. In most of the households that I knew, the mothers and fathers quarrelled with one another and both of them quarrelled with and thrashed the children. No doubt, there were some happy and peaceful families in Railway Terrace and Tramway Buildings but happiness and peace were quiet things which escaped my observation while family quarrels were noisy affairs, often conducted in the public of the backyards where they could be observed by all.

It had never occurred to me that all those quarrelling mothers and fathers or that my own silent mother and father had come together from choice. Choice had no part in life as I knew it. Life was a matter of being born a Railie, going to school at five and leaving it at fourteen and everything that one did of one's own choice, like going to visit one's granny or reading books in the wash-house was a disobedience and a sin.

The knowledge that my mother and father had once upon a time chosen to marry and live together bred in me a deep dark sadness. It meant that they had once been in it together, as I myself had once been in the Rounders game in the Home Park, but they had been put out of it, as I had been put out of the game. Down the years, between the time when my mother was a tablemaid at Laurelbank and my father a ploughman at the Castle Home Farm and this time now, something between my father and mother—it might have been like the thing that I had felt between Mr. and Mrs. Adair when he stood beside her chair by the fire—had died.

In a way, they themselves had been responsible for its death but, in another way, they were not. My mother's desire to get rich and improve her circumstances had been part of the death, but even my granny, who was so wise, agreed that it was praiseworthy to try to improve your circumstances. My mother, when she persuaded my father to stop being a ploughman and work for the railway company, had destroyed something in him or was it he who had destroyed something in himself by allowing himself to be persuaded, just as he was destroying himself still more by getting drunk all the time now? But when my mother persuaded my father to become a railway worker, she did not know what effect the change would have upon him. Children were better behaved when she was young, she was always saying and so, probably, she had never seen the bleak black dreariness of the forbidden territory of the railway siding, as I had seen it. It was not only my mother that had made my father different. That grim sooty railway siding had changed him too and probably many other things had caused changes in both my mother and my father, things it was impossible to know about, even inside your head, changes like that made by the presence of the Iron Man in our house, which was something too subtle even for thought.

Until now, my mother and my father had been the governing powers of my life, not people but powers. My mother governed in the day to day things like 'Can't you wipe your feet when I've just scrubbed the close' and 'Don't pick your nose it's vulgar' and my father governed through the pay packet that bought my food and kept me in house and home. But now that I knew these new things about them, things borne in on me by my granny, the Adairs and my own senses, my mother and my father were powers no longer. They were merely two people at the mercy of circumstances as I had been when I had had to leave the game of Rounders in the Home Park—at the mercy of circumstances and of themselves, I had to amend. After all, I could have stayed in the Rounders game on sufferance, if I had allowed Isabel to fight Violet Bryson and send her from the field bleeding and in tears. The more I thought about it, night after night in my chairbed, the more my mother and my father looked like the lamb with the sore leg that Mr. Adair had picked out of the flock into the shelter of his arm but, although I was learning for Bible the hymn that went:

> *Loving Shepherd of Thy sheep,*
> *Keep me, Lord, in safety keep—*

there was no evidence of a strong arm that would rescue my father and my mother. And, after all, they were not lambs. Lambs did not know what was what and lambs did not get drunk and then be vulgar in bed. Even if the strong arm were there, I decided, people were not so easy to rescue as lambs.

CHAPTER FOUR

The world looks very beautiful
And full of joy to me;
The sun shines out in glory
On everything I see;

HYMN 575

WHEN I WAS EIGHT YEARS OLD, what history has chosen to designate as the 'Great War' began and my father went away to it, along with a great number of other Railie and Trammie fathers. It was splendid fun for us children, the Saturday forenoon that these men came home from work early, laughing and joking and strangely excited, as if they were about to embark on an 'up Lochview'. They came swaggering up from the railway siding and the tramway depot into the pub round the corner from Railway Terrace and we children gathered round the pub door and heard big Jock Stewart tell how he had told the Works Manager that he was off to the war and that the Railway Company could shove its engines up its arse. I could never remember such gaiety among the men of Lochfoot and this gaiety was infectious, travelling from Jock Stewart to all the other men as the brown spots of impetigo travelled from face to face round the classroom at school, only the men did not have ugly brown spots but laughter, a loud care-free energy and a proud swagger such as we children had never seen in them before.

Although my father spent quite a long time in the pub, he was not drunk when he came back to our house at dinner-time. While we ate our herring and potatoes, he did not speak but that was not unusual and it was only when he took his good boots out of the cupboard under the sink that my mother became aware that anything strange was happening. Nowadays, my father never wore his good boots. Instead, he

67

seldom bothered to lace his dirty old working boots but shuffle-clopped his way home from work to pub and back to house with them flapping round his ankles.

'Ye can't wear your good boots to the siding!' my mother protested shrilly.

He looked up from the boots. 'I'm not going to the siding. I'm done with it. I'm off to Glasgow to join up.'

'Join up? You're off your head! What about *me*?'

'You'll be right enough,' he said and began to take his good shirt and suit out of the kist.

No more was said. Dressed, he rejoined his friends in the pub until it was time for the train they were to catch when they all, some of them accompanied by their wives and followed by us children, went down to the station in a joking disorderly throng. My mother was not among the women who came to the station because that would have been vulgar.

Down there, Beery-belly was standing with his big stomach sticking out and although he allowed the womenfolk to follow the men on to the platform, he would not let any of us children go through, so we ran away up to the stone bridge that carried the road over the railway. From up there, we watched the train come in, the men go on board and the train pull out again with a puff-puff-puff and a loud clanking. We watched it rattle away along the steel rails, growing smaller and smaller and then it curved itself into a sinuous semi-circle and disappeared into the black hole of the tunnel. As it went from sight, it blew its whistle and the sound came back to us as a thin wail and at that sound all the gaiety drained away. I suddenly did not know anything that was happening except that my father and all the other men had been carried away to an unknown place inside the steel snake of the train and I knew that all the other people had the same frightened, empty powerless feeling that I had. We all turned away from one another, silent, as we were after a raid up Lochview but with fear and not contentment in the silence and the women who had shouted and laughed their way to the station were silent too until one by one they began to cry and turned homeward, their shoulders drooping under their woollen shawls.

That evening, I could see that my mother considered it very vulgar of my father to have gone away to join up like this but as time passed, her attitude changed. It was a creditable thing to have your man away fighting for his king and country, as it was called and my mother was very uppish with Miss Miller whose old brother just went on, in an inglorious way, being a railway guard.

If I tried to think seriously about the war, I became very confused. I could not imagine my father fighting for his king and country. He did not even know the king and the only country he had known since the time I went to school consisted of the railway siding, our kitchen and the pub. Even when drunk, my father was not a fighting man and I was sure he would not fight for the railway siding or our kitchen. Maybe he was fighting to save the pub from the Germans for it had been the only place he cared about for the last few years.

On the whole, however, from the point of view of the child tribe, the war was a good thing, for it caused changes in Lochfoot and made a break in the monotony. It also made authority less vigilant of our activities because it seemed to make old Beery-belly and old Loco busier than they had been formerly, while the womenfolk in the closes of Railway Terrace and Tramway Buildings had things to occupy them that they had never had before.

These things were called 'telegrams' and the post office now took on Pete Johnson, who had left school just before the war started, and provided him with a fancy uniform, a little round hat and a red bicycle. Pete cycled round the town with his orange telegrams in a little leather pouch on his belt and when he was first appointed, we all used to shout 'Tellypete!' and run after him, making catcalls until he out-distanced us. Not long after he got his uniform and his bicycle, we were running after him down the main street one day when he suddenly swerved in his showy way round the corner and into the backyard of Railway Terrace and along to the close where the Aitkens lived. Mrs. Aitken hap-pened to be standing at the close mouth at the time with her baby in her arms inside a grey woollen shawl that went round both the baby and herself and wee Tommy and wee Bessie were sitting on the step at her feet. She merely stared at Tellypete when he offered her the envelope and he had to open it and tell her what it said and then another woman took the baby while Mrs. Aitken sat down on the step, threw her dirty blue apron up over her face and began to make loud wails such as I had never heard anybody make before. They were more like the wail of the train going into the tunnel that day my father went away than any human noise.

When Tellypete had come into our backyard, all the women had come out to the close mouths and now a lot of them gathered round Mrs. Aitken and eventually went into her house with her, while others carried in wee Bessie and wee Tommy who were howling too. I was beginning to feel like crying myself because it was all so strange and frightening, so I went back along the yard to our close where my mother and Miss Miller were standing on the step and went in behind them. They were so busy staring along towards Mrs. Aitken's that they did not even see me and I waited quietly for them to say something that I could overhear and which might explain this queer thing that was connected with Tellypete. What was in this little orange envelope of his that could cause such an uproar?

My mother and Miss Miller stood in silence until Mrs. Anderson, who had been in the crowd around Mrs. Aitken, came hurrying along and said: 'It's Aitken. She's just beside herself, poor soul.' Mrs. Anderson hurried in through our close, went upstairs, came down again with a whisky bottle under her apron and hurried away along the yard. It was a custom of the Terrace that a woman never carried a whisky bottle except under her apron, although I did not know why, because you knew automatically that anything concealed in this way was a whisky bottle. Only after she was out of earshot did my mother speak.

'Poor Aitken,' she said to Miss Miller, 'he was a good soul.'

'Aye,' Miss Miller agreed with her and then because, as my mother said, she seemed to think that through playing the organ in church she was almost a minister herself, she added: 'God rest his soul.'

I went along the close into our kitchen. Mr. Aitken was dead. He must be, for my mother to say he was a good soul and for Miss Miller to speak words that belonged to old Poopit. Mr. Aitken had been one of the biggest drunks in the Terrace, a vulgar fighting drunk at that, so vulgar that he had had to go to Court once and pay a fine. It was only after people were dead that my mother and Miss Miller spoke of their souls. I looked up at the Iron Man. Was that how it was? Did you turn into a soul after you were dead?

My mother now came in and I said: 'Is Mr. Aitken dead?'

'Yes,' she said, 'and if I see you running after Peter Johnson's bike again in that vulgar way, you'll suffer for it.'

'Is Mr. Aitken a soul up in Heaven now?' I asked. 'Or has he gone to Hell?'

'Hold your vulgar tongue! Poor Andrew Aitken was killed at the war, fighting for his king and country and it's very sad. Now, off you go, out of my road.'

But she was not sad and Miss Miller was not sad either. I went out to the yard and looked along at the crowd of women talking excitedly around Mrs. Aitken's close mouth. They were not sad either. Indeed, the whole backyard was full of excitement, that excitement half-ashamed, half-lascivious that used to hold everybody in thrall some Saturday nights before Joe Murphy went to the war. Mrs. Murphy was one of those vulgar women who accompanied their husbands to the pub and when Joe had had a win on the horses and they had plenty of money, they would both get drunk. Then they would have a fight when they came back home. On these occasions, what my mother called 'bold' people gathered closely round, as the women were round Mrs. Aitken's close mouth now, the better to see the proceedings between the Murphy pair while people who knew what was what, like my mother and Miss Miller, stood back at a distance as they had done today.

'Isn't it disgraceful?' Miss Miller would say. 'Somebody will have to get the policeman to them again.'

'Disgusting,' my mother would agree but neither of them were disgraced or disgusted by the Murphys, any more than they felt any sadness about Mr. Aitken today. There was in them too, although they stood at a distance, a similar shamed enjoyment of a happening in the backyard as there was in the 'bold' people who crowded round the close mouth.

For me, the war took on the guise of a distant, very powerful new circumstance that could reach out a long snake-like arm and suddenly change the whole face of life and not all the changes it made were sad and ugly like the day that Tellypete called at the Aitken's house.

One of the things which the war caused and which was of great interest to us children was the advent of the 'steamies.' These were lorries of a kind we had never seen before. They had a fire burning inside them at the front, with the smoke going out through a funnel above the driver's cabin and underneath the cabin there was suspended a circular tray to catch the hot cinders that fell down from the fire. They came along by the Castle wall and past the school gates, carrying great loads of tree trunks to the railway station, tree trunks which were needed somewhere because of the war. When they came clanking past the school playground, when we

72

were out for morning or afternoon interval, we all clambered up behind the iron railings on top of the wall to shout: 'Steam, steam, stinky steamie!' in a way that was half-derisory, half-admiring, the way in which all primitive creatures react to something of which they are uncertain.

One day, as we were all going home the half-mile or so along the road for our midday dinner, cuffing and throwing stones at one another as usual, the news ran through the mob that one of the steamies had had an accident and, all thought of dinner forgotten, we took to our heels and made for the long hill that ran down by the Castle wall to the railway station on the outskirts of the other side of the town. When we reached the site of the accident, I felt inside myself that shameful sort of excitement that had held the backyard while Mrs. Aitken had wailed with her apron over her face, because I was going to see the dead driver of the steamie, all broken and bloody, lying in the road. As we swept in a tide down the hill, I felt a shudder of reluctance too, an uncertainty that I really wanted to see this dead man but, in the heart of the human tide, it was not possible to turn back. But there was no dead man. There was only old Beery-belly who had three stripes on his sleeve now, Lochfoot requiring more policing because of the war and his young, thin gangling constable who was already known to us as 'Macaroni'. These two stepped into the middle of the road to stem our rush and to tell us, of course, to 'get away home out of it' but before we went we took a good look at something that was new under our young sun. The Castle wall was breached. Where the twelve-foot, stone, mason-built, impenetrable un-see-over-able wall had been, there was a gap about ten yards long, ragged at the edges and sitting on a fallen coping-stone was the cheeky young driver of the steamie, unhurt, smoking a cigarette and looking very pleased with himself at the centre of this drama. Behind him, inside the gap, his vehicle lay on its side, still sending a defiant wisp of smoke up through the green branches of the beech tree it had felled as it turned over and under the big iron wheels, which lay in flat circles on the ground was a carpet of unbelievable blue, made by the fallen heads of thousands of wild hyacinths. The blue stretched away under the arches of the beeches where the sun streamed through in long shafts, lighting the grey of the trunks to silver among the limitless blue that faded into a blue distance. This was my first recognition of beauty, my first experience of that painful swelling of the heart as the mind tries to encompass and absorb the message conveyed by the eye.

Because the steamie had given me what was, I thought, my first glimpse of what lay behind the Castle wall, I repaid the steamies by being polite to them. When they passed by the playground after the accident, I clambered up behind the railings like my fellows but I shouted 'Steam, steam, steamie!' in cheerful greeting, leaving out the word 'stinky', in the hope that yet another of them would crash through the Castle wall. The wall, of course, was repaired by the Castle masons within two days but the masons could not blot out of my memory the blue of the hyacinths under the beech trees. But no steamie ever again crashed through the Castle wall. What happened was not what I had hoped for but something very different.

One morning, early in the summer holidays, a few of us were gathered outside Gardiner the Cobbler's shop, deciding how we would spend the forenoon. Mr. Gardiner was away at the war by now and Mrs. Gardiner herself was doing the cobbling which, being something new—imagine a woman soling boots!—caused us to loiter by the shop door.

Wee Sammy Gardiner came out to join us. He was only about four but he had the right to be in it at some of the minor tribal activities and we all paid him a certain respect because unlike any of the rest of us, he owned a dog, a mongrel called Ginger, a most enviable possession. Sammy was very generous with Ginger and would let anybody speak to him or pat him and consequently Sammy was allowed to join in ploys that would have been barred to many four-year-olds.

So there we were, about a dozen of us loitering on the pavement when a steamie came round Pillans's corner and along towards us. We all lined up along the kerb ready to shout at it but, after that, I do not know what happened. Ginger ran into the road, Sammy ran after Ginger and then they were both lying between the huge iron wheels, Sammy quiet and pale and still, Ginger all writhing and bloody and making horrible gurgling cries until the butcher ran into the road with his big knife, bent over Ginger and the cries stopped.

Sammy was away for a long long time and when he came back, he had a steel brace on one leg which was much shorter than the other and he could walk only with the help of a crutch. He could not be in it at any of our ploys any more but sometimes when I thought of it and had nothing better to do, I would tell him a bit about what was going on and what our future plans were. The thing that I did not tell him or anybody else was that I did not shout at the steamies any more. I climbed on the playground railings or stood by the kerb when they went past, but my voice did not join in the shout of 'Steam, steam, stinky steamie!'

By the summer holidays of 1915, I was nine years old and this was a momentous age in the Lochfoot child community. At nine years old, one was eligible in the summer holidays to go Up-the-Burn-to-the-Dam, which was the final rung in the ladder of tribal custom.

It was said that the Free Masons who went to church on their special Sunday with the funny little aprons worn in front of their trousers had secrets, secrets that they never told to anybody, not even to their wives, but no secrets were ever so securely kept inside any society as were the secrets of Up-the-Burn-to-the-Dam among the child tribe. All I knew about it, before I became eligible, was that it was the greatest

75

possible sin against authority but all the details were shrouded in mystery until the great day of my initiation. After this, I would be truly 'in it' with the child tribe, with access to all its inner councils.

The expedition was planned, guerrilla fashion, behind the wash-houses of Tramway Buildings, where there was a dank alley that stank of urine and worse. There were only two initiates, a boy and myself, because it was reckoned that more would endanger the enterprise and I knew that it was an honour to have been chosen in preference to several other nine-year-old girl claimants. I listened carefully to all the instructions about doing what I was told, staying with the crowd and such like and then the leading boy said, looking sternly at the other novice and myself: 'But if ye hear this—' he put his forefingers in his mouth and gave a piercing two-noted whistle '—it means it's old Stink an' you're on your own an' ye better run for it for if he catches ye, he'll leather ye black an' blue with his stick.' We had all been squatting, our heads close together, but now the leader stood up, the rest of us did likewise and suddenly the air was rent by the piercing whistle. All those who had been Up-the-Burn-to-the-Dam before had whistled in chorus and the leader said: 'You pair have to learn the Stink-whistle before ye go up again. Mind that. Right, come on!' We set out from the dark alley into the summer evening. As instructed, I went alone by a roundabout route to the bridge over the road at Pillans's corner.

'Just walk as if ye weren't goin' any place in partic'lar,' the leader had told me, 'but be at old Pillans's by the time the kirk clock strikes seven. If ye see anybody else on the bridge 'cept me, turn back an' waste some time.'

As I always did when going nowhere in particular, I hopped part of the way, skipped some of it and gave a little passing cheek to the man at the Co-op and when I came within sight of the bridge, only the leader was there, sitting on the parapet, dropping stones down into the water but, further along the road towards the school, I could see Maisie Anderson and Molly Murphy, strolling along with their arms round each other's waists. They were in charge of me on the expedition and at the thought of its imminence, my stomach gave a sickly little heave. The three of us met on the bridge and before I knew what was happening Maisie was over the parapet and had dropped down the six feet or so on to the grass strip beside the Burn and the leader and Molly had me over the wall too, suspended by the arms above what seemed to me to be a bottomless pit like Hell.

'Let go!' said the voice of the leader and I was falling, my knees scraping painfully down the stone of the wall but Maisie was below to break my fall and I was standing on the slimy grass beside her, when Molly dropped down beside us. 'Come on,' said Maisie and we were running in single file along the strip of grass beside the sewer. As we ran bare-footed along the slime, I was almost crying with the pain of my scraped knees while blood ran down my shins but my mind was distracted from the pain by the horrors of the sewer on my left. I had never been so close to it before and we had now reached the part where the drains of Railway Terrace and Tramway Buildings discharged. There were dead rats, partly eaten by the live rats that were swimming among the yellow froth, pools of grease and clots of sodden newspaper; the stench was like a blow between the eyes and with rising horror I saw that, ahead of us, the grass verge was coming to an end, leaving no way forward except through a tunnel floored with the terrible rat-infested black water. This, although I did not know it, was the underside of the bridge that carried the road round the corner of Tramway Build-ings. The moment came when, pulled from in front by Maisie, pushed from behind by Molly, I had to leave the slimy grass behind and step into the water, I shut my eyes, felt the coldness on my feet, waited for the rats to brush against my legs but they did not come. After wading forward for a long time, Maisie released her hold on my hand which made me open my eyes. She was climbing through a huge iron grille that hung down from the stone-work above to water level and as soon as she was through, she began to pull me after her while Molly pushed from behind. Except for this one hole, which had been cleared by the forward members of the expedition, the grille was loaded with branches and rubbish of all kinds which had been brought down by the Burn and among it there was the rotten carcass of a rabbit, crawling with maggots, which made me shut my eyes again. When I opened them, I was standing knee-deep in clear water, my back to the grille with its load of horror and hanging in front of me there was a spray of wild roses which trailed in the water below while, above, it made a web of palest pink and palest green between me and the pale blue sky.

Such was the entrance to the wonderland of Up-the-Burn-to-the-Dam.

That evening, I did not penetrate as far as the Dam. I lingered by the side of the Burn, so that my guardians willingly forgot me, after warning me not to wander far alone lest old Stink should see me and so that they would find me easily for the return journey. I sat by the sparkling water, washing my bloody knees and had no inclination to wander far because there was so much so see where I was. There were things which I had not known to exist, the fat heads of wild pink clover, the shy blue of tiny violets that grew beside a grey boulder and then there was the Burn itself. It was beyond comprehension that this clear water, sparkling over white pebbles and round grey stones could, beyond the iron grille, turn into that noisome slime on which here and there, the vile yellow scum floated like islands until they were fragmented by the noses of the swimming rats. Lying on my back, looking up at the sky, I came to know for the first time that the sky could stretch above the world like this, unbroken by the outline of a roof, a chimney-pot or an iron clothes-pole.

Expeditions Up-the-Burn-to-the-Dam were made no oftener than fortnightly, and were made up of no more than twelve people at a time I was to discover, and it was now that I made my first breakaway from the laws of the child tribe. I was now a full member of the group which had the right of entry to the alley behind the Tramway Buildings wash-houses where discussions took place about Burn and Dam, but I did not want to discuss them or merely live over again that one expedition which, according to tribal law, might be the only one I was 'picked to be in' throughout the entire summer. I wanted to be Up-the-Burn, not sitting in a stinking alley talking about it and, one Saturday afternoon, I did not join my fellows after dinner but ran straight down to Pillans's corner, climbed on to the parapet, shut my eyes and dropped down over the wall.

This time, I did not even notice the swimming rats as I ran along the slippery grass, because the magic world beyond the iron grille was before my eyes and when I reached it, I made my way right up the side of the Burn to the Dam itself. This was almost past all belief. The Dam was round, still as a sheet of looking-glass and fringed with willow trees that hung over the water above their own reflections, except at the part where there was a wall of stone and the smooth water flowed over like a glass curtain, fringed at the bottom with foam lace where the water splashed into the Burn. I spent a long hot afternoon around the Dam and only after I had climbed through the grille on my homeward way did I remember that it is simpler to drop down over a six-foot parapet than it is to climb up and over such a barrier without assistance.

Before our first expedition, the leader had impressed on us this very hazard of the return journey, the need for haste on the part of a 'wee smout' like myself when I had to climb on to Maisie's bent back and be hauled up by the leader him-self from above.

'We're not going to skitter about and get seen by old Cock or old Beery-belly just because you're too bliddy wee for nine,' he had said.

It seemed that when I broke away from the laws of the tribe by going Up-the-Burn by myself, I had also broken away from some of its immemorial wisdom and here I was, too bliddy wee for nine, on the sickly grass, trapped by the Castle wall on one side, the wall of old Pillans's place on the other and the six-foot parapet in front of me, broken only by the conduit pipe full of sewage that led away under the road above. I had a moment of panic, when walls and parapet seemed to close about me, to be about to grip me in a stone prison of circumstances from which there was no release, until I noticed that the wall on Pillans's side was as dilapidated as the rest of his property, so that the mortar had fallen away between the stones. If I could cross to that side, I could climb up and over by finger and toe holds between the stones but here, at the mouth of the culvert, the dead rats and excrement formed a thick clot. Still, there was nothing else for it and Up-the-Burn was worth it. I put my skirt inside my knickers, my bare feet into the filth and waded forward, the slime growing deeper until it was above my knees, but at last my fingers found a grip between the stones of old Pillans's wall. It was simple now. Soon my eyes were peering over the top into the scrapyard and in another second I was safely over, making my silent way through the heaps of old iron to the break in the wall by the road where the gate should have been.

Having found this way, which I kept as my own secret, out of the magic and forbidden world, I began to make trips Up-the-Burn nearly every day during the summer holidays, foregoing them only when an organized expedition was to set out from the alley behind the wash-houses. Being of no great intelligence and child of the backyards and pavements as I was, I had little bump of locality so that I did not realize that, once through the iron grille, I was in the grounds of the Castle. To me, the Castle grounds were still that limitless expanse of blue hyacinths and beech trees which had been exposed when the steamie broke the wall down near the station, over two miles away from the grille as the crow flies. When I was Up-the-Burn, I was in a place known only to myself, a place away and apart and in another dimension from Railway Terrace, Tramway Buildings, the Village, Lochview Crescent and the Castle. Yet, all the time, my mind was alert for old Stink with his stick and although, in the part of my mind that stored facts, I knew that Stink was the Castle gamekeeper who guarded the forbidden territory, the idea that I was inside the Castle wall did not come to birth.

For a long time, I was content to confine myself to the gorge of the Burn and to the willow trees that fringed the Dam, to the territory marked out by the tribe as fair game but, one day, near the Dam, I came upon a little path that led away through the trees and I followed it. It was an August day and the trees were in full leaf and the birds in full song and with a prickle of high adventure down my spine, I cautioned myself not to leave the path in case I might get lost. I would merely follow the path for a little way and then return to the known territory round the Dam. But there is a fascination in a winding path through wood-land and another and another corner kept beckoning until I rounded one last corner and saw, a few yards ahead of me and with a sickening sinking of the heart, that well-known recurring feature of Lochfoot, the Castle wall. There it was, behind the tree trunks, invading and limiting this beautiful world, the twelve-foot-high mason-built wall and at its foot, the little path, defeated in its meanderings, turned at an angle and ran parallel to it, in its grey shadow. I could not believe it. I walked right up to it and placed the palms of both hands against it, pushing at it to make sure of its rigid reality and immovability. It was as rigid and implacable as any Iron Man. My sadness was as crushing as if a ton of that masonry had fallen over on top of me.

Standing there, with my hands against the rough stone, I suddenly knew that I had always hated this wall, that I hated all walls, all the barriers that were such a feature of Lochfoot, walls round the backyards, walls round the school playground, walls round the railway sidings, walls, walls, walls. culminating in this massive Castle wall that intersected and towered over all the other walls, going wherever it wished to go, like some monstrous stone snake, cutting its unscalable trail of slime through every other barrier with arrogant disregard. Standing there, I wished that all the steamies in the world, driven by their cheeky young men in greasy caps, would come clanking along and drive their iron wheels through every inch of it but, when the moment of passion was spent, I knew that this would never happen. The wall had always been there and would go on being there for ever.

Looking up from my puny height at its tall pride, I wished that I had remembered to bring my stolen piece of school chalk with me. The only weapon that I and my kind could bring to bear against all these walls was to write on them, write the worst words we knew. If I had had my chalk, I thought, I would write a word I had never written before, I would write it over and over again, the word that only the biggest wildest boys wrote and they wrote it only seldom, the word that began with F. 'F— this wall!' I would write, but I had not my chalk with me. You did not bring wall-writing chalk Up-the-Burn with you.

I was about to turn, defeated, away, when I had a sudden idea that I could attack the wall in a way that it might like even less than being written upon. I could look over it from here and that would be a blow struck against the very reason for its existence, because it existed in this monstrous height for the very purpose of not being looked over. Here, unlike all the other parts of it I had seen, there were trees beside it. Get up a tree and look over. Better still, choose a tree close to it, get up and sit on top of it, do a pee on top of the bloody thing, in fact. In two seconds, I was in the branches of a beech and dropping down to sit on the wall. In my first moment up there, I was mentally giddy with achievement and power. Here I was, on top of the hated barrier, making it kiss my arse, as Bessie Mellon said to the boys when they shouted names after her and it was only after the giddy glory had abated a little that I remembered that I had come up here primarily to look over. So, now, I looked and nearly toppled from my perch at the strangeness of it all. I was looking down upon a place that I knew, yet a place that I had never seen before and it was some little time before I recognized the school playground, looked down upon from the wall at which I had always, hitherto, looked up. In another few seconds, I realized that the Burn, the Dam, all the beauty I had known were inside the Castle wall like the blue hyacinths that the steamie had exposed, but that did not matter. I could still get in through the sewer, the tunnel and the iron grille and, with a defiant thrill, I realized that I could get out again at almost any point, at any time I chose, without being caught and without wading through that clot of filth at old Pillans's corner. To prove it, I dropped the twelve feet on to the concrete of the school playground, landing on my bare toes with my knees bent, for I was a highly skilled wall-dropper by now.

Thereafter, I regarded the Castle grounds as my own kingdom and it was a huge kingdom, not only to someone of my size but by any standards. It covered an area about four times the size of the whole township of Lochfoot and at its centre there was a circular park in which stood the Castle itself. I spent long hours looking at it from various forms, like those made by hares, which I had made for myself in the undergrowth at the edge of the surrounding woods. The Castle was enormous and seemed to me to be the ultimate in almost unbelievable grandeur. I know now that Lochfoot Castle is a hideous ostentatious edifice in Victorian baronial style, a huge ill-proportioned pile of grey stone, topped by a forest of pepper-pot turrets, so that the entire mass resembles more than anything some monstrous fungus, parasitical upon a dung-heap of such festering richness that the turrets, burgeoning in rank excess, crowd one another as they reach upwards for air. But, gazing at it from my form in the undergrowth, it had a magnificence beyond anything I had ever imagined.

Sometimes, a motor car came round the corner and stopped at the door and a man came out and was driven away by a liveried chauffeur. Sometimes I saw a movement, a curtain being adjusted behind one of the tall narrow windows. These things happened at the front, where the horrible iron lions guarded the big wooden door, but I had another form quite close to the gravel drive at the other side and from here there was plenty to be seen. The baker's van would come clop-clopping past me and in through a gate to a yard and while the horse shook its bridle, making a jingling noise, the baker's man would balance on his head a great wooden tray of bread, rolls and the like and carry it in through a door. In this backyard, there was always something going on— maids in blue and white hanging out washing, gardeners going to and fro with baskets of vegetables and flowers and there was one young gardener who was very clever at sneaking up behind a maid who was tipping out a dustpan into a dustbin and pinching her blue-clad behind, so that she began to scream and giggle.

The more familiar with the Castle grounds I became, the more careless I became so that I forgot all the tales I had heard of old Stink and his stick that could beat you black and blue. One day, late in August, I had made up my mind to cross the fourth and last of the driveways that intersected

84

the grounds, so that there would no longer be any segment of the huge kingdom that I had not traversed. Successfully, I crossed the dangerous exposing snake of gravel from under-growth to undergrowth and began to make my way through an unexplored forest of beeches but, as time went on and the sky changed colour towards evening, I began to feel a slight prickle of anxiety. I had been in the grounds since just after dinner-time, had not bothered to go home for tea, feeding on brambles instead, but now there was an emptiness in my stomach and a growing eeriness in the woods as I looked about me. Surely, soon, I must come to one of the other drives, find a bit of the wall or see a tree that I had seen before but no recognizable landmark appeared. The ground was rising, I was conscious of going uphill and I did not like to think of turning back the way I had come because the darkness was beginning to gather thickly among the trees down below.

At last, the trees thinned and I was on a grassy place that sloped away below me down to a group of buildings where a light showed in the misty blue of evening. Beyond this, there was an open space, then another row of lights, then a black snaky line that came from the distance and led to a place with a lot of red and green lights, behind which was a blackness, broken by many many lights. I suddenly realized that I was looking down upon the Castle Home Farm, the Home Park, the Village, the railway and railway station and the whole town of Lochfoot. I could also see a great stretch of the Castle wall. It came slanting down the hill far on my right until it reached the end house of the Village. The Village *became* the wall for its length and then the wall proper took over again and ran all the way to the side of the loch. Then there was the town, lying as if in a saucer at the loch-side, with Railway Terrace at the end furthest from the water and Lochview Crescent at the opposite end, on the rim of the saucer where the ground began to rise again. On the side of the loch beyond the Crescent, the Castle wall rose again, curved right round the back of the town and disappeared into the distance like a snake going into a hole, unbroken except for the four driveways that I knew to exist and the railway and the road with its tramlines that lay below me. The railway and the road also looked like snakes from here, steel snakes, I thought, the only snakes strong enough to withstand the stone snake of the wall.

'Hi, you!' said the voice and there, emerging from the trees a few yards away, was the forgotten old Stink, waving his stick.

With the instinct of a hunted hare, I ran not downhill into the open but uphill into the cover of the woods and a nightmare chase began. At that time, I had never seen a hare hunted but I had the instinct of the hare to double this way and that and to stay still in cover while, all the time, as I listened to old Stink crashing about in the undergrowth, I was panting in my mind: 'The wall! The wall!'

The wall, of which there had seemed to be so much when I stood looking out over its sinuous length, now seemed to be very elusive but at last it was ahead of me, dim but solid in the gathering dark. Like a monkey, I swung up and on to the branch of a beech, sprang up from there on to a higher branch and from it to the top of the wall, just as old Stink came rushing like an angry bull at the trunk of the tree. With a spray of beech leaves between my face and his, I said tauntingly: 'Ta-ta, old Stink. Shove your stick up your arse!' and dropping down on the far side of the wall, I ran until, exhausted, I fell down among the foot-high heather of the hillside.

When I could look around me, it was quite dark and I had no idea how to get home. I knew that I was on the hill above the Castle Home Farm but how to get back over that wide hostile territory to Railway Terrace? It was then that I thought of the wall again, that circumscribing circumstance at whose mercy—or the mercy of circumstances like it—I had been all my life. But I was no longer at its mercy. It was at mine. I had scaled it hundreds of times and now it was going to lead me home. Retracing my steps through the heather, I placed my left hand on it and thus guided, I made my long way down to the end of the Village and from there back to the Terrace.

My mother was angry with me, of course, not because she had been worried about me but because that uppish interfering Miss Miller had remarked that she had not seen me all afternoon and where in the world could I be.

'I could have told her you would turn up like a bad penny,' my mother said, 'but you needn't think you'll get any supper here at this time o' night. And don't you be as late as this again or you'll suffer for it. It's vulgar to be out raking about like a tinker till this time o' night, that's what it is, just plain vulgar.'

I did not care about her slap or her scolding for the afternoon and evening had been worth it, especially ending up by giving cheek to old Stink and using the wall to get home by and everything. My mind was bursting with knowledge and triumph and power. Against myself, with my body that could climb and my mind that could think, that Castle wall was impotent.

In my chairbed, inadvertently I began to sing out loud:

> *The world looks very beautiful*
> *And full of joy to me—*

'Be quiet this minute, you!' said my mother. 'Anybody would think you were as daft as old Kingdom Come the Trammie. You'll be singing hymns at the pub door next. How often have I told you it's vulgar to sing hymns except in the right place?'

CHAPTER FIVE

O what can little hands do
To please the King of Heaven?
The little hands some work may try
To help the poor in misery;
Such grace to mine be given.

HYMN 670

THE ONSET OF WINTER exiled me from the land of the Burn and the Dam. With winter, the Burn became a roaring torrent that foamed and swirled from wall to wall, covering the strip of grass on the Castle side and piling up against the parapet at Pillans's corner, where the conduit pipe could barely take its flow. The wall frowned down, impregnable from the outside; the tall iron gates stood shut in front of the neat little lodges and it did not occur to me that, to gain access to the magic land, all I had to do was to go down to my granny's house, go out through her back door and jump over the low ferny wall into the Home Park. In my mind, there were many ways out of the wonderland but only one way in and that one way was now closed by the winter spate. In any case, I was at school from morning twilight until evening twilight on most days and there would be no point in being Up-the-Burn when it was too dark to see the sky and the trees. I rejoined the child tribe and took to the streets and alleys of the town for the winter.

Tellypete was still dashing about on his red bicycle but nobody followed him nowadays, although he delivered more telegrams than ever. He was simply part of 'the war', this curious backdrop to our lives whose main feature was the novelties that it brought. Tellypete had been a novelty for a little while but now we had a new one that came from nobody knew where, which was simply suddenly among us.

This was a singing game, but a singing game with a difference. We girls had always played singing games like 'Bee-baw-babbity' and 'London Bridge is falling down' among the clothes-poles of the yard until Miss Miller or somebody came to tell us to 'get away out of it with all that noise' but in this new game, the boys joined too. It was not so much a game as merely singing and sort of dancing. You turned your toes out as far as they would go, carried a stick in your right hand and twiddled it round and round while you clumped along on your awkward feet, singing:

> *The sun shines bright on Charlie Chaplin,*
> *His boots are crackin', for the want o' blackin',*
> *His wee baggy trousers need a mendin'*
> *Before we send him*
> *To the Dardanelles!*

None of us knew who Charlie Chaplin was but we knew that the Dardanelles was 'at the war', because the fishmonger's son had been killed there, but it was a fine cheery song and we sang it all the time. In this way, the war was always throwing up something new and different.

One afternoon, when we were released from school, the intelligence spread among us that 'something was doing down at the Arms'. This was a ramshackle old building down near the railway station where the Burn, after almost encircling the town, flowed into the loch. It was practically derelict, with boarded-over windows except for a small section at one end, which was one of Lochfoot's many public houses and which was run by an old couple who lived in one room behind the bar.

My mother said that all pubs were low and she described the Arms as the lowest of the low and it was indeed so low in interest that we children never bothered with it. Even its patrons were so low in numbers that Beery-belly never had to settle fights there and neither the Salvation Army nor

Kingdom Come the Trammie bothered to play or sing songs of redemption outside its shabby door.

At the news of something doing there, we all ran down in our customary disorderly rabble to have a look and sure enough, there was something doing.

There were slaters repairing the roof, joiners putting glass in the windows and painters and plasterers working inside but none of this was of much interest to us children so, having given some cheek to the workmen and having kicked over a few buckets that were lying about, we took ourselves off. We continued, however, to keep watch on the place for, in our minds, all of Lochfoot was our territory and it was our serious business to observe any development that took place.

In quite a short time, the Arms began to look quite smart, with the lettering of its full name 'The Lochfoot Arms' re-painted in shiny black and my mother heard it said that it was to be a hotel for officers coming home on furlough from the war, officers from Australia and Canada and places like that whose homes and families were too far away to visit on a short leave. Somebody who had the capital to do the Arms up like this, my mother said, knew what was what and was on to a good thing.

Sure enough, one Saturday the officers began to come and not only Australian and Canadian ones. There were some English and Scottish ones as well and I was rather puzzled about their families being far away. The officers did not have their children with them but they had their wives, with whom they walked arm-in-arm across from the railway station and the wives were very gay, all laughing and giggling and beautifully dressed with feathery hats, quite unlike any of the wives in Lochfoot, quite different, even, from any of the wives of the rich men of Lochview Crescent. And the Arms became more and more gay, more and more attractive to us children, as the laughing ladies waved to us from the windows or went tripping off Down-the-line in the train with their officer husbands but, in the contrary way that life often seemed to work, the more gay and attractive I found the Arms, the more my mother disapproved of it, until one day she said: 'Don't you dare to mention that vulgar place in this house again and if I hear of you going down there, you'll suffer for it.' But, of course, I did continue to go down to the Arms. Everybody went and it was tremendous fun.

A curious development that I began to notice was that, although a different lot of officers arrived every Saturday, the ladies stayed on at the Arms and that the lady called Doris went off on trips Down-the-line with a different officer every week. Yet, this was not too surprising either, because Doris was the nicest one of all the ladies down at the Arms. She lived in a room on the ground floor and when the shutters were not closed over her window, she often sat behind the open sash, wearing her sealskin coat if it were cold, chatting to anyone who came along. She was a very friendly lady, the friendliest person I had ever met, friendlier even than Mrs. Adair and very very kind.

One day, when we were all hanging about, a fight broke out among us as fights frequently did and a stone thrown by somebody hit me, making a cut in my forehead. This ended the fight. Fights usually ended when blood began to flow, that is if they were casual fights like this one and the others all ran away, leaving me crying and bleeding on the pavement. Then, right in front of my nose, I saw two legs in black stockings and a flurry of white lacy petticoats swinging over the ground-floor windowsill of the Arms and there was Doris, with her arms around me saying: 'There now, don't you greet, pet. In the name o' the Kingdom o' Heaven, when I get hold o' the wee bugger that threw that stone, I'll murder him, so I will,' and then she spat on her white handkerchief, cleaned my forehead gently and kissed me. This was the first time that anybody had ever kissed me and it was beautiful to be kissed by Doris. She was a bit like Mrs. Adair, all soft and cushiony but, of course, she had this lacy pink blouse and this rustling black shirt over the white petticoats instead of Mrs. Adair's dark print and tweed and she smelled like the wild roses up the Burn.

'What's your name, pet?' she asked.

'Jean. Jean Robertson.'

'Well, Jeanie, you wait a minute and Doris'll get ye a penny,' she said and in a whirl of petticoats she went back through the window and after a minute she leaned out and gave me a silver threepenny bit.

After that, I used to go down every day and wave to Doris at her window if her shutters were not closed and every time now she would open the window and sit inside while a group of us stood on the pavement and we would have a long chat with her. She was different from all our mothers and all our teachers at school and Sunday school, different from simply everybody. It was difficult to describe the different-ness of Doris, even inside your own head where you do not need words. You could not say what she was, only what she was not. She was not against you, she never said 'Don't' or 'Stop it' and I did not think I had ever heard her say the word 'no' but she often said 'yes' or 'aye', rather. That was her form of greeting. 'Aye, aye, there!' she would call to us with a cheery wave of the hand when she saw us coming towards her window and when, as sometimes happened, a voice called from inside the Arms saying: 'Doris, you're wanted', she would call back: 'Aye, aye, Ah'll be there in a minute!' She needed the minute to give us all pennies before she closed first her window and then her shutters.

From time to time, I had observed with interest, some members of the child tribe crossed the invisible line that divided the tribe from the hostile adult world on the other side. Boys tended to cross the line more suddenly than girls. On Prize Day, while the rest of us watched the Villagers collect the prizes, a boy would be among us, a member of the tribe and the next day, when we of the tribe were embarking on our destructive two months of summer freedom from school, that boy would be seen, carrying his piece-bag, on his way to work at the Tramway Depot, a member of the adult world.

With the girls, the metamorphosis was more gradual. It first began to show in their changed attitude to the school water closets where we spent a fair amount of time at the intervals, especially in winter when it was cold and wet. Older girls stopped playing the game of peeing fancy patterns on the stone floors and instead began to collect in huddles of two or three in one closet to indulge in the pastime known to us younger ones as 'talking blood' and when a girl, usually about the age of twelve, gave up this pastime too, her manner took on some of the characteristics of the adult world and it was whispered among her fellows that this girl had 'got it.' Sadie Fraser had recently got it and looked very much like a miniature of her own squint-eyed sour-faced mother when, one evening, she halted me in the street just after Doris had given me a penny before closing her window.

'Jeanie Robertson,' Sadie said, 'if I see you talking to that sinful woman again, I'll tell your ma.'

'Just you try it, you dirty big clype!' I told her. 'I'll talk to Doris if I like.' But I was frightened in spite of my defiant words. Sadie Fraser was now part of that hostile complex of parents and authority. The unwritten but meticulously kept law of the child tribe, the law that forbade one to 'clype', the law that laid down that the only answers to questions from all representatives of hostile authority were no, nothing, nowhere and I don't know no longer applied to Sadie. If she told my mother about my talking to Doris, it would no longer be clyping. It would be an act within the law of the hostile world to which she had gone over and there was nothing I could do to stop her perpetrating this act. However, since she had gone over to that world, Sadie merited the traditional treatment that the tribe meted out to it, the giving of cheek.

93

'Doris!' she said scornfully now. 'She's a *bad woman*, that's what she is.'

'She's not. She's a lot better than your skelly-eyed old ma!'

Jeanie Robertson, that woman is a *hoo-er*!'

'Ach, away an' boil your can!' I said and ran away along the street. What was a hooer?

Perhaps the greatest unfairness about the hostile adult world was that it knew much more than you did and it would never share its most important knowledge with you. It would tell you about God and teach you to spell and do sums and sing hymns but it would not tell you why Doris, who never did any work, always had pennies to give to children and money to buy lovely clothes and scent. Why did my mother say that Doris and all the ladies at the Arms were vulgar? Why did Sadie Fraser say that Doris was a *bad woman* in that queer voice when Doris was so good to all us children? What was a hooer?

Eventually, in the course of a conversation in the school water closets, I discovered that 'whore' was the name given to women who did That for money, the which information muddled my mind still further for, as everybody knew, all women did That for money, so why speak the words in a hushed voice? All the women in Railway Terrace and Tramway Buildings, except the old maids like Miss Miller, had got married and did That with their husbands so that they might have homes of their own and a pay packet on Saturday night, if their husbands did not drink it all, that is. And everybody knew that Miss Miller was not an old maid from choice. She would have liked to be a whore like all the other women and have her own home and pay packet instead of living with her brother. For the life of me, I could not understand why Doris and all the other ladies at the Arms had to be spoken about in hushed voices in the water closet when everybody knew that most grown-up people did That and that the only trouble about it was that it made you have

94

babies which you did not want. I made up my mind that everybody was simply jealous of Doris and her friends because they could do That 'all day as well as all night if they are asked to' and at the same time they were clever enough not to have babies. People always said that a thing was bad or vulgar if it was something that other people had or could do and that they had not or could not do themselves.

However, Sadie Fraser went away to domestic service, nobody else felt sufficiently interested to tell my mother of my friendship with Doris and I went on seeing her, along with my fellows of my own age. The older girls of about twelve were beginning that process of change towards the adult world and no longer hung around the Arms in the evenings or on Saturdays, but they spent all the school intervals in the water closets, gossiping about Doris and her friends, just as all our mothers spent their spare time gossiping at close mouths and on stairheads about Doris and her friends.

To my mind, the ladies at the Arms were the brightest and most beneficent influence that had fallen upon Lochfoot in my lifetime. Quite apart from the pennies and sweets which they gave to us children, they were a spot of musical cheerful colour among the drab brick walls and dark iron railings, especially after Doris acquired a gramophone with a bright pink horn that sent rousing military marches and dreamy waltzes out into the street from her open window. And, in addition to the pennies, sweets, music and colour, they kept the Railie and Trammie women so busy being scandalized that there was no time for stairhead rows about Mrs. Ferguson leaving the wash-house boiler dirty or Mrs. Anderson blocking up the water closet again. All day now, the stairheads and closes held knots of women in drab tweed skirts with shawls round their shoulders, talking in hushed voices about these shameless women. Doris and her friends even ousted Mrs. Grey the Railie from her long-held position as a subject of hushed-voice conversation. That Mrs. Grey's husband, when drunk a Saturday, had been known to 'get on top of her seven times in one night' was something paler than insignificance compared with the women who did That all day and all night too 'with one man after another.' This last phrase too, I thought, was another indication of jealousy among the Railie and Trammie women. I could understand any man wanting to do That with Doris, to get close to all that cushiony softness and lovely smell but no man, I thought, would want to do That with the women at the stairheads, except that it was something a man had to do and once he was married, old Beery-belly would take him to prison if he did it with anybody other than his wife. In Deuteronomy, in the Bible, which we read in the water closet at school, it said that men should be stoned to death when they did That with the wrong women but we being more civilized nowadays than the people in the Bible, had Beery-belly to take them to prison instead.

I loved Doris just as she was but, once or twice, I thought it would be nice if she had a baby, because she was a bit like Mrs. Adair in a queer way and I felt sure that she would love a baby and cuddle it all the time. A baby would not be a nuisance to her because she never told all of us to get out from under her feet so, one day in the school water closet, when the big girls were talking about Doris's latest new lace blouse, I said: 'It would be great if Doris had a baby.' The big girls stared at me with round eyes and then burst into raucous roars of derision.

'Away ye go out o' here, ye stupid wee scunner!' one of them told me. 'Grass disnae grow on a weel-trodden street.'

It took me some time to understand that this meant that if you did That too often, all day and all night, for instance, no babies came but this merely led to more mental muddle. Why did not Mrs. Riley, whose husband was not at the war because of his wooden leg, not do That a bit more frequently? If she was 'expecting again and her with nine already' as I heard my mother tell Miss Miller, it was her own fault, the stupid fool.

One Saturday forenoon in the late spring of 1916, a group of us went down to the Arms, hoping to have a chat with Doris at her window but when we arrived there, the whole place was shut up, locked and dead, with not a lady or a frilly petticoat to be seen anywhere. The other girls were disappointed, but they did not care as much as I did, but then I do not think that Doris had ever kissed any of them as she had me. I was heartbroken. I had always known that anything that was nice did not last for very long but there had never been anything as nice as Doris, except dinner at the Adairs and that she should go away like this, without even saying that she was going, was the worst thing that had ever happened to me. Not having any more dinners at the Adairs was reasonable, after what my granny had told me and it would have been reasonable if my mother had locked me in the house so that I could not go to see Doris but for Doris just to go away was not reasonable. After all, she was grown-up and neither the whole world nor all its circumstances could make her go away if she did not want to go. So Doris must have wanted to go away. She was tired of talking to us and of giving us pennies. She did not care about us any more and she had gone away, taking all her lovely gay friends with her.

I came dragging back to Railway Terrace, with no desire to join any group I met on the way, with no desire to go Up-the-Burn, even, for nothing in the world seemed to be worth doing. As I came round the corner into the backyard, I was close to the wall, dragging my bare toes miserably through the dust and fluff from beaten carpets that collected in the angle between bricks and ground and as I made my silent approach to the close mouth, I heard the voice of Miss Miller.

'—and four policemen, my brother said, came with a Black Maria and took the whole boiling away Down-the-line.'

'When?' came my mother's voice.

'Just after seven in the mornin'. My brother's on the early work train just now.'

'Well,' said my mother with satisfaction, 'if that doesn't serve them right, the shameless hussies!'

'Shameless you may well say,' said Miss Miller. 'They were laughing and joking with the policemen, Jim said and one of them was winding up a gramophone with a red horn in the back of the Black Maria.'

'A *red* horn?' said my mother. 'The vulgarity!'

I had heard enough. I ran away and hid behind the wash-house boiler while anger seethed inside me. So it *was* the whole rotten world of authority and circumstances that had made Doris go away! She had not *gone* away. She had been *taken* away—taken in a Black Maria, taken to prison. It did not bear thinking about, Doris in prison. They would take away her lovely pink lace blouse and rustling skirt, put her into a long grey baggy dress and shave all her hair off. That was what happened to you in prison, the big girls said. This must not be but what could I do? What in the world could I do to help Doris? What could a stupid wee scunner like me do against all the might of Beery-belly, all the grown-up world and its authority?

Suddenly I remembered some words from the hymn we were learning at Bible:

> *O what can little lips do*
> *To please the King of Heaven?*
> *The little lips can praise and pray—*

Behind the wash-house boiler, I said my first prayer. Every morning at Bible and every Sunday at Sunday school, we did a thing called saying prayers when we had to clasp our hands, bow our heads, shut our eyes and say: 'Our father Wishart in Heaven—' and a lot more stuff and nonsense, when everybody knew our fathers were really called Robertson or Riley or Adair and that they were not in Heaven at all but at the war or down at the siding or out looking after the Castle sheep. At Sunday school, though, the teacher had said once that if you prayed to God to forgive your sins, he would do it. I had never tried it because any sins that I had done that had been found out, I had had a thrashing for already and did not care whether they were forgiven or not while it was just stupid to ask to be forgiven for things that had not been found out. How did you know they were sins at all, most of the time, until they had been found out? But if God was as good and helpful as they all said he was, there was no harm in asking him to do what he could for Doris, so, doing the thing properly, I got down on my knees on the concrete in the cramped space behind the boiler and prayed as hard as I could: 'God, I praise you like anything. God, please don't let them put Doris in prison. Don't let them shave her hair off. And God, if you can manage it at all, make her come back to the Arms for ever and ever Amen.'

I prayed this prayer, or one very like it, many times and in many diverse places and although it was the first prayer that I had ever really prayed, it was answered. Two weeks later, on our way home from school, there rose from the ground the cry: 'The Arms is working again!' and we all ran down there as hard as we could. Breathless, on the road outside the window where Doris, her hair curlier than ever, sat in her pink blouse beside her pink-horned gramophone, I remembered even amid all the excitement to thank God for bringing her back.

Later on, these dramatic departures of Doris and her friends in a Black Maria became a commonplace but, now, I knew that God would always look after them and see that they came back.

It was only much later that I discovered that the ladies were fined a small amount, the licence of the Arms changed into another name and Doris and her gramophone re-rented the room that looked out on to the street, that she might obey the British battle-cry of that time which was 'Business as usual.'

My mother did not come to know of my friendship with Doris which may, on the face of it, seem unlikely in a comparatively small place like Lochfoot but it must be remembered that my mother's stringent economy forbade her to go visiting as most of the other women did, having tea and gossip in one another's kitchens, for this would mean that she would have to return hospitality. The only time I remember her having a cup of tea in another house was on the day that I deposited the water closet paper on Miss Miller's parlour carpet and she considered, for this was how her mind worked, that Miss Miller owed her a cup of tea because she had removed the offence from the carpet with the coal tongs. At the dictates of her economy, my mother's orbit was a very narrow one, taking her no further from her own kitchen than to the shops round the corner in one direction and to look in at the window of Pillans's Secondhand in the other.

It is also possible, however, that she did know of my loitering around the Arms and decided to ignore it. Her attitude to me was one of dutiful detachment. She fed me within the framework of her economy and she kept me scrupulously clean, which was not easy in school conditions in which one beguiled the tedium of a boring lesson by counting the lice on the woollen jersey of the girl in front. My clothes were mended and not allowed to fall into rags like those of most children and my fair wispy hair, which Mrs. Adair had admired so much, was small-tooth combed every day and washed every Saturday night. Yet, in spite of all that she did for me and all the time that she expended on me and my physical welfare, there was always the underlying certainty in my mind that I was a nuisance. If I were not there to be cleaned, mended for and generally looked after, my mother would have more time and money left over to contribute to her economy. I had a certainty that my mother did not look after me because she liked to do so but because it was vulgar to have children and not look after them, like that vulgar Mrs. Murphy, who did nothing but sit on the step at her close mouth, kissing her latest baby while the rest of her large brood ran free, wild and lousy.

And so it is possible that my mother knew of my loiterings in the vicinity of Doris and decided to ignore them. To try to stop this activity would mean confining me to the house and the backyard where I would be within her sight and, if I were in the house, I would be 'always under her feet and making a mess' while, if I were confined to the yard, I would be swinging myself giddy round an iron clothes-pole or writing on the walls with my stolen chalk, to the outspoken annoyance of Miss Miller. I did not consider my mother wicked and I would have fought any of my fellows who tried to say a word against her, but I always knew that she preferred to be alone and not have me under her feet all the time.

This was all to the good from my point of view at this time, for it meant that I could visit Doris unimpeded and enjoy one of the happiest times I had known. Doris was always gay, had no economy, found nobody vulgar and in the midst of the wartime shortages, which gave my mother the excuse to be ever more frugal, Doris always had sweets and pennies to dispense through her window to us children.

As time and the war went on, Doris and her friends made fewer trips in the Black Maria because, I imagine, Beery-belly and his colleagues had more important things to do and adopted an attitude of *laissez-faire* to the goings-on at the Arms. This, in the tortuous way that things happen, drew Doris closer to us children than ever for, now, when she had time to spare, she would come out for short walks with us, unafraid of the shadow of the law. On these occasions, I used to long for Beery-belly or Macaroni to pass on their bicycles for Doris, dressed in her feathery hat and feather boa, was as good at giving cheek as any of us.

'In the name—' she would say, using the shortened version of her favourite oath which was 'In the name o' the Kingdom o' Heaven' '—in the name, here's that old bladder o' lard on his byke! Hi, Beery-belly, mind ye don't split yer troosers!' In this way, she taught us many new and engaging insults to hurl at our adversaries.

Only once did I see Doris angry and compared to this the frequent anger of my mother was a poor, pale starveling thing. The anger of Doris was a tempest which called up all the elements of earth, air, fire and water and set them rumbling, tumbling, roaring and rolling in a chaos that threatened to overwhelm the world. It happened on a bleak wet Saturday forenoon when a throwing-out was about to take place in an alleyway near the Arms. Things were quiet around the Arms on Saturday forenoons, as a rule, because one lot of officers went away on the early morning train and the next lot did not arrive till mid-afternoon, which was very convenient, for it meant that Doris and her friends and we children were all free at the same time.

We were talking to Doris at her window on this forenoon when old Joe from Pillans's Secondhand came past, wheeling his long flat barrow and somebody said: 'It's a throwing-out! Come on!' Most of the crowd on the pavement ran away after Joe but I did not go. I did not like throwing-outs very much and preferred to stay with Doris.

'What's up? Where're they off to?' she asked me.

'It's a throwing-out,' I explained, watching old Joe and his barrow turn the corner into the alley.

'What's that?'

I found it difficult to explain. Everybody in Lochfoot knew what a throwing-out was but Doris was so different. She knew all sorts of things that Lochfoot people did not know and other things, that Lochfoot people knew, she had never heard of.

'That was old Joe with the barrow for the furniture,' I explained. 'The Rent Man'll be there an' they'll throw the folk out an' old Joe will give the Rent Man the rent an' take the furniture an' stuff to old Pillans's Secondhand.'

'But what about the folk? Where'll they go?' Doris asked.

I shook my head. 'I don't know.'

Doris sprang up, ran to the door of her room and shouted along the passage: 'Lucy! Belle! Gracie! Come on! Never mind your stays! Hurry up, I want you!' and then she was back and out over the windowsill into the street. 'Stay there an' show the rest where to come,' she ordered me and was off along the street to the corner of the alley.

By the time that Lucy, Belle, Gracie and I reached the scene, the woman who was being thrown out, along with her two children and her baby, was already in the street, Doris was talking to the Rent Man in his dark blue suit and old Joe was putting a battered wooden cradle on to his barrow. It was now that Doris became angry, now that the Heavens opened and the elements began to rage. She seemed to swell to enormous size, to tower high above the roof of the little house, to fill from side to side the narrow cobbled alley.

'Put that cradle back in that hoose, ye dirty old bugger!' she roared at Joe and strode towards him so that he cowered away around his barrow.

The Rent Man now went towards her, saying something but she swung round, her arm extended at shoulder level and gave him a clout that sent him spinning against the wall.

'*Po*-lis! *Po*-lis!' Old Joe shouted, as if he hoped that Beerybelly would hear him even if he were up in Lochview Crescent.

'Shut yer mug, ye old bastard!' said Lucy and she, Belle and Gracie advanced on the barrow, seized the cradle and carried it back into the house.

Doris now had the Rent Man by the front of his coat collar and was shaking him like a dirty old carpet, while she said: 'Thirty shillin's, is it? Ye'd put a wumman an' three weans oot in the rain for thirty shillin's? Christ, I'll murder ye, so I will!' And the threat was not idle, The Rent Man, his throat restricted by her grip, was gasping and gagging when Lucy, Belle and Gracie gathered round Doris and made her release him.

'Jeanie,' she said to me now, her eyes glaring, her chest heaving, 'run down for my purse. It's in the top drawer o' the dressin' table.'

When I came back with the purse, she was calmer. She took out the money, handed it to the Rent Man and said: 'Gi'e that to yer miser o' a boss, ye miserable snivellin' wee shit an' tell him I hope it chokes him,' and then she was once more the Doris that we knew as she turned to the woman with the baby: 'Come on, Missus, come in the hoose afore the wean gets its death oot here in the rain.' Lucy, Belle and Gracie, however, seemed to have decided that, having been called out half-clad on this miserable morning, they might as well make a day of it and, helped by the children, they loaded old Joe and the Rent Man on to the barrow and wheeled them, amid loud jeers and taunts, out of the alley and away down the street. I stayed with Doris and the woman and the children.

'My money'll be here any day now,' the woman said, 'an I'll pay ye back. It's three weeks since Willie went to France an' the Sergeant Doon-the-line says it takes aboot a month. I'll pay ye back, honest to God I will.'

'Ach, yer backside!' said Doris, opening the purse again and taking out a pound note. 'Here, send the wee lassie up the street for some stuff. An' if that old bugger wi' the barra comes back, send for me. I'm just roon' at the Arms, there. Come on, Jeanie.'

We walked back to the Arms together, where Lucy, Belle, Gracie and all the other children were recounting to one another with much merriment how they had tipped the Rent Man and Joe out of the barrow into a pool in the gutter of the main street and had left them there. Doris did not join in the merriment but climbed quietly in over her windowsill and sat down on her chair.

'Thirty shillin's,' she said. 'Jesus! The greed, the bliddy greed! In the name o' the Kingdom o' Heaven, if there's one thing I canny abide, it's greed! Lucy, away ben to the bar and bring us a drink an' some biscuits for the weans.'

With her glass in her hand, she sat quietly, looking out and upwards, over all our heads at the grey drizzly sky. Her eyes were wider, deeper, darker than I had ever seen them and forever afterwards, when I thought of Doris, I would remember her eyes that day and find myself thinking about the Kingdom of Heaven.

CHAPTER SIX

When from Egypt's house of bondage
Israel marched, a mighty band,
Little children numbered with them
Journeyed to the promised land;
Little children
Trod the desert's trackless sand.

HYMN 573

WITH THE COMING OF DORIS and all the other interesting things
that the war brought into the life of Lochfoot, I began to
hope that it would never end. I thought now and then on
the time before the war, before Doris came, before I was old
enough to go Up-the-Burn-to-the-Dam and wondered how I
had managed to put up with circumstances so lacking in
interest. Sometimes, if I was alone in the street and Tellypete
sped past on his bicycle, I would think of my father and even
wonder if, one day, there would be a little orange envelope
with the address of our house on it, but the thought was as
vague and unreal as the memory of my father himself. I could
not remember what he looked like or form a mental picture of
him although I could call up clearly in my mind the image
of the black snake of the train disappearing into the tunnel,
while I could hear again the sad wail of its whistle. These
thoughts came seldom, however, and did not stay with me for
long.

Lochfoot these days had a prosperous air and there was
always something of interest happening in the streets. Somewhere Down-the-line, a furlough camp had been established
for colonial troops and many of these men came to the public
houses of Lochfoot or to visit Doris and her friends at the
Arms. Like Doris, they were different from all the other
adults we knew in that they would chat to us and give us

pennies for sweets, so that we hung about the railway station and the tramway terminus to cheer them when they arrived instead of giving them cheek. Indeed, when the need arose for the giving of cheek, the soldiers were more accomplished in this way than we were.

Two of the Lochfoot people to whom the war brought great prosperity were old Sandy the Tinker and old Tipperaray. Sandy the Tinker lived out at the camp at the Old Dam in a tent made by a tarpaulin draped over his little cart and around this nucleus lived the many generations of his descendants. Sandy played the bagpipes for a living. My mother said that all tinkers were just shiftless scum that never turned an honest penny in their lives but they were cheerful happy sort of people, even before the war came to brighten things up. Tipperaray was not a tinker but my mother said he was shiftless scum too because he did not do anything except play his melodeon, mostly a tune called 'It's a long long way to Tipperaray' and get drunk with the pennies that people gave him. Sandy the Tinker got drunk quite often too but there was nothing unusual in that and I, inside my head, thought that to play the bagpipes or the melodeon for money to get drunk with was more cheerful and sensible than working your guts out down in the railway siding for money to get drunk with.

Sandy the Tinker and Tipperaray naturally found out too about the soldiers coming in from Down-the-line on the trains and tramcars, so they took to arriving in the station yard with their bagpipes and melodeon. When a train came in and the soldiers started to come out into the yard, the bagpipes would strike up and we children would start to dance what we called the 'Hooligan,' a sort of reel that we always danced when Sandy was there with his pipes and then Tipperaray would play his melodeon and we would all sing.

One Saturday afternoon, we were all there and a train came in and the soldiers who came out of it all began to dance and sing along with us, instead of just giving us a few pennies and going off to the pubs. Instead, when Sandy's and Tipperaray's whistles needed wetting, two of the soldiers went over to the Arms and came back not only with some bottles but with Doris and some of her friends and soon we were having a proper ball in the open space between the station and the tramway terminus.

Naturally, old Loco came out of his office and old Squeak came across from his and we children stopped dancing and collected a few stones to throw at them before making our getaway but when old Loco shouted: 'Here, you lot, get away out of it!' a big Australian with his hat turned up along one side went over to him and said: 'You speakin' to us, you old sod?' and Loco backed away. Beery-belly and Macaroni were sent for but that did not do any good either. In the end, some soldiers took Beery-belly, Macaroni, Loco and Squeak on to the big turntable for turning the engines round and held them there while more soldiers turned the table round, faster and faster, while Doris and her friends and we children and even Loco's two porters and ticket clerk stood watching, laughing until we nearly burst our sides.

We might have been paralysed there, laughing for ever, except that now another train came in and, instead of soldiers, there came out of it and into the yard a little group of women and some frightened-looking little children with round dark eyes. The turntable stopped turning, the laughter died away, the two porters slunk into the station and Beery-belly, Macaroni, Loco and Squeak quietly made off, hoping they were invisible but nobody was even looking at them. All eyes were on the little group of people at the door of the station building. They looked so lost, forlorn and queerly foreign, standing there huddled together.

Old Joe from Pillans's Secondhand now came trundling his long flat barrow into the yard and the two porters piled on it a few bundles and boxes before Joe trundled it away again, the sad little group walking in his wake. At any other time, we children would have followed the little procession to find out where it was going, but on this day we stood silent alongside Doris, her friends and the soldiers. It was suddenly a grey October afternoon, going on towards evening and Sandy the Tinker's red tam o' shanter, even, seemed to lose its colour in the still misty light. For a long time, nobody moved or spoke until Hector, Sandy's dog with his tin mug hanging from his neck, decided that it was time to take up a collection and began to walk round the group on his hind legs. Her eyes still on the people who were following old Joe up the road, Doris held out her hand to the big Australian soldier.

'Got a few coppers, Digger?' she asked.

His eyes still on the people going up the road, he took a handful of change from his trouser pocket and gave it to her. Doris dropped a penny into Hector's mug and distributed pennies to all us children before handing back to the soldier the larger silver coins that remained. He turned to look down at her now.

'These poor buggers of Belgians,' he said. 'Can a man get a drink in this town, girlie?'

Doris smiled at him, took his arm and they went away over to the Arms, followed by her friends and the other soldiers. That was how the Belgian refugees came to Lochfoot.

As we of the tribe drifted out of the station yard and up towards the town, we were silent. We had not the vocabulary to deal with a happening as strange in our lives as this, for the Australian soldier's remark to Doris meant nothing to us. It had conveyed nothing that had not penetrated to our minds already, for we could see and feel for ourselves that the members of the little group were 'poor buggers.' We had to assimilate the sad strangeness and the strange sadness of what we had seen and felt, until a place emerged in our scheme of things for this new group of people. I, in common with my fellows, had heard of the invasion of Belgium by the Germans.

We had been told about it at school but we all had a natural resistance to anything we were told in the classroom. Also, I in common with my fellows, had heard talk of the terrible happenings in Belgium at the close mouths of Railway Terrace, but anything that 'folk' like your mother and Miss Miller said was taken with more than a pinch of salt. They said that the Germans killed Belgian babies and did That to Belgian women who did not want it done to them but think of the rubbish that my mother and Miss Miller talked about Doris and her friends. They were now calling them 'scarlet women,' although they had never even been down to the Arms to see them because, they said, they would not lower themselves by going near that terrible place. Doris was not scarlet but creamy coloured with big dark eyes and very beautiful. Thus, as we made our way up through the town that Saturday evening, none of us connected the little group of women and children who had come on the train with Belgium.

It was on the way home from school on the following Monday afternoon, just as we were passing old Pillans's place, that the cry rose out of the ground: 'Here, there's folk down at the Paddies!' and at once we all went rushing in a mob up past the shops, round past Railway Terrace, past the gable of Tramway Buildings and on down towards the tramway depot. Between the depot and the railway siding was the building known to us as 'the Paddies,' a long, narrow two-storey building which had once housed the itinerant navvies, most of them Irishmen, who had constructed the railway and had laid down the tramway lines. This building, of the prevalent sooty brick, had never housed anybody in my lifetime for, by the time I was born, the paddies, as the Irish navvies were called, had moved on to convert fresh woods and pastures new into steel-railed permanent ways.

Unlike all the other unoccupied, not to mention occupied, buildings in Lochfoot, however, the Paddies had escaped the ravages of the child tribe but this was only because it had no eatures that could be damaged. Built to house the roystering drunken navvies, the glass of the small ground-floor windows as well as the glass of the sky-lights which lit the upper floor was protected inside and out by close-meshed wire netting and there it stood, an impregnable block of dirty brown brick, rectangular, with a heavy wooden iron-studded door in the middle of one of its long sides. It was here that we now gathered in a silent staring crowd for the door was open for the first time in our lives. Inside, we could see a stone staircase with iron railings leading from the hall to the upper floor and the hall was littered with some of the bundles that had been on Joe's barrow and there were also pieces of iron bedsteads and rolled-up mattresses, the belongings of people in transit which always look so pathetic. Household gods lose all their majesty when taken out of their honoured places and into alien territory.

Soon we saw women coming and going across the hallway and up and down the stairs, picking up the boxes and bundles and carrying them away out of sight. They were strange different-looking women, different from the Lochfoot women and different again from Doris and next the strange different-looking children began to peer at us round the sides of the big wooden door, children younger than most of us and with the big scared-looking eyes. Then we heard the women calling to the children in a strange quick tongue, a language far more incomprehensible than that used by the Tinkers when among themselves but, before we could see any more, Beery-belly had to arrive and tell us to get away out of it. We retired before him, as we always did, slowly, tauntingly, throwing a shower of stones at him while we shouted: 'Old fat Beery-belly, mind ye don't split yer troosers!' and the children inside the big door began to look less scared, even to smile a little, as if they understood our need to treat Beery-belly in this way.

It was through eavesdropping on my mother and Miss Miller that I discovered that the people who had come to the Paddies were called Belgian refugees and now another of these curious incomprehensible attitudes of the adult world made itself manifest. I had often heard my mother and Miss Miller and many other people, including my school teacher, talk about poor little Belgium and gallant little Belgium and Miss Miller was the one who told most of the blood-curdling stories, which her brother had heard at first hand from soldiers, about the terrible things that the Germans did to the Belgian women and children. But now that the Belgians had come to the Paddies, there was no more about poor little Belgium and gallant little Belgium.

'Disgraceful,' Miss Miller said, 'letting them live down in that place. They've no business in Lochfoot at all. They are very dirty people the Belgians, I've always heard. They live next door to the French and eat frogs and snails, and everything.'

'They seem to be a queer vulgar lot right enough,' my mother agreed and she told me that if I went near those dirty foreign Belgian brats, I would suffer for it.

In the event, we of the Lochfoot tribe did not fraternize with the Belgian children of whom there were perhaps half a dozen in all, but only because they were too young to run with our gang, the eldest of them being about three. But we gave a measure of our attention to the 'Belgies' as we called them, for they were very interesting to us, being so very different. They were interesting and different in every way, from their strange language to the strange savoury cooking smells that emerged from the small windows of the Paddies and the strangest thing of all was that they were always happy, it seemed. The women sang as they swept the floors, sang as they washed clothes in two big wooden tubs out of doors and they were always picking up the children, giving them kisses and setting them down on their feet again.

Then, one day, a fence went up round the rough sooty grass and weeds that encircled the Paddies, so that we interested enquirers could no longer get so near to the door, but no sooner was the fence in position than the women began to dig and in no time at all they were planting vegetables. In a staring ring round the outside of the fence, we looked on fascinated and there was an older very fat lady who was the first to speak to us when she said: 'Fine day, yes?' At this, we were all so overcome that we ran away but, of course, we were drawn back as if by a magnet, for never had we seen women digging and planting before. After a day or two, I and some of the others took courage to return her greeting and soon we were calling 'Nice day, Madame Fenchel!' over the fence for we had discovered that, queer-sounding as it was, this was her name.

One Saturday morning, we were all at the fence chatting to her when the baker's cart came down to the Paddies and while the Belgie ladies were gathered at the back of it, buying their bread, did not that awful old horse of the baker's that would bite you as soon as look at you, lift its tail and deposit a great light brown heap of shit eggs right in front of the clean doorstep? We, of the outside of the fence, were so ashamed of that horse that we began, staring at what it had done, to back away from Madame Fenchel which made her look round in the direction of our horrified stares, whereupon she made a long crying noise: 'Ah-ah-aaaah!' of sheer delight, rushed away, scooped up the whole heap on a spade and began to scatter it with great care among her cabbages.

One day, shortly after that, May Spence and I were passing the door of the Co-op when that old horse did the same thing again in the roadway and May, giggling, said to me: 'It should've kept it for Madame the Belgie!' and it was then that I got the idea that sent May and me sneaking up the Co-op close to the place where the empty boxes were kept to pinch one and two bits of wood to use as scoops, whereupon we scooped up the heap and took it down to Madame as a present. Nobody was ever more pleased with any gift and she rewarded us with two large pieces of very tasty cold sausage, handed the box back to us and indicated that a similar gift would be welcomed and rewarded at any time.

The earth round the Paddies was mainly rubble and cinders from the railway siding where nothing but rough grass and weeds had ever grown but, by the time the war ended, it blossomed like the rose, for all of us knew that whenever we had an urge for a piece of cold sausage, all we had to do was to find a present for Madame Fenchel. The baker's cart, the coal lorry and any other horse-drawn vehicle was pursued by a child with a box or a bucket and two of the bigger boys, with great daring, acquired an old perambulator, took to the farm fields away out beyond the Tinker Camp and sold the cargoes to Madame for threepence.

The discovery that Madame and her friends liked to eat eels was an accident. It was the habit of some of the bigger boys, when they went Up-the-Burn—in spite of our attentions to Doris and the Belgies, we still went on with our time-honoured ploys—to catch an eel if they could and use it like a whip, to chase us girls and the younger boys. We all ran screaming from the snaky, rubbery dead thing and the bigger boys regarded this as the peak of high entertainment. When you were being chased by an eel, it was policy to run towards the town. It was the only time when you wished to encounter someone in authority, such as old Beery-belly, because when the uniform appeared, the chaser would have to dispose of his eel over the nearest high wall or be caught holding in his hand the evidence that he had been trespassing Up-the-Burn.

On this day, we who were being chased had forgotten, in our eel panic, that there was now a fence round the Paddies for, hitherto, across the rough grass and round to the door of the tramway depot had been the quickest route to a uniform if we had failed to meet Beery-belly on our way through the town. So, now, we found ourselves trapped by the brick wall in front of us, the Paddies fence on one side, and the railway embankment on the other side while, behind us, was the snaky horror of the swinging eel. Fortunately, Madame Fenchel was in her garden, where she spent most of her time and our panic died away as we heard her call the eel-swinger towards her and begin to bargain with him in the broken English which she had learned mainly from ourselves, so that her language was a mixture of French and Glasgow-Scots. The eel-swinger that day was one of the roughest of our rough tribe but Madame beat him down from an outrageous one-and-sixpence to ten-pence for his eel and he had to take the tenpence because he knew that the rest of us were about to give him away. We all knew, you understand, that an eel was not worth anything at all, that it was no use for anything except to chase people with and that the minute anyone in authority saw you with an eel, it turned at once from an asset to a liability. I, along with many others, therefore, thought it was a shame to take money for an eel from what my mother called 'an ignorant Belgie' and now that an adult was involved, the mob began to mutter angrily against Mickie Murphy, the eel-owner and chaser. So Mickie gave up the eel and received his tenpence, saying: 'Thanks, missus, but don't tell the *polis*,' whereupon Madame said 'Comment?' and we all became involved in trying to explain.

'Don't tell Beery-belly.'

'Hide it from Beery-belly.'

'Comment?'

'The policeman.'

'The man like this,' and somebody gave a life-like imitation of Beery-belly puffing along on his bicycle.

'Comment?'

She had gathered at least that the eel was a secret and had it folded inside her apron when the tramways superintendent appeared at the corner of the depot building.

'No tell *him*!' somebody said, pointing.

'Celui-là? Non! Yah!' said Madame and spat furiously in the direction of the superintendent who had already, it seemed, done something to displease her.

In such ways did Madame Fenchel extend our culture a little so that we all became very fluent in this phrase and extremely apt at the spitting part in our future dealings with Beery-belly and the like and in return we tried to broaden the education of Madame. We assisted her with her shopping in the early days, going with her to the grocery and to the butcher's shop which she found most puzzling, with all the black blood puddings and white oatmeal puddings done up in circles like little fat snakes, items with which she was unfamiliar. On the last Saturday forenoon of each month, too, Madame Fenchel and the white-haired oldest Belgie lady of them all had to go to Glasgow, to fetch their money, we understood, from some office there and to pay their rent for the Paddies to another office. On these occasions, we conducted them to the station where, prodded in the stomach by the umbrella of Madame, old Loco would have to let us into the booking office, that we might buy the tickets and then on to the platform, that we might see our friends comfortably ensconced in the train.

By this time, we had come to know that all the Belgie ladies were related, all members of one family either by blood or marriage, so that the one called Antoinette was the niece of Madame Fenchel and the cousin of the one called Madeleine. Madame Fenchel was the niece of the very old one with the white hair, who was lame and could walk only slowly with the aid of a stick but this old one was very important and controlled the money on which they lived. She did not do any of the cooking or cleaning or gardening but sat all the time in an old wooden armchair in the kitchen corner when it was cold and wet and in the garden when it was fine. She was always dressed in black and had beautiful jewellery, dangling ear pendants with purple glass in them, a big brooch with a lady's head in white on brown at her throat and round her neck a long chain of gold links with pearls in between from which hung a gold watch that was pinned to the breast of her black blouse with a brooch which was a true love knot made of pearls. Madame Fenchel and all the others referred to this lady, who always smiled to us but never spoke, as 'Grand' mère', which we pronounced 'Grammar,' so that I was a little as red of her but not because of anything she had ever said or done to me. She was connected in my mind with a school lesson that I could never understand and for which I was always having the strap.

We also educated Madame as to what was good and what bad in the life of Lochfoot, introducing her to Doris and the ladies at the Arms when we took her shopping and making her understand that old Beery-belly was just a useless old bladder o' lard who would put you in prison as soon as look at you.

One evening, we were chatting to Madame over her garden fence when who should appear, taking a short-cut home from the tram terminus, but old Pillans. Madame, who was a friendly person and proud of the new language she was learning from us, liked to greet everybody in her second tongue and she now stopped weeding and came close to the fence. We children at the same time backed away across the road to the embankment side, getting ourselves as far as possible from the path of old Pillans.

'Nize evenin', yes?' said Madame brightly, but the shambling figure in the long black coat, the head down, slithered furtively and wordlessly past and away round the corner out of sight.

'Who?' asked Madame indignantly, pointing with her trowel at the corner as we all rushed back across the road.

'You don't speak to *him*!' we all shouted at once.

Madame looked uncomprehendingly from one angry, roundeyed horrified face to the next.

'Silly-wee-la! Non! Yah!' we all said in chorus and spat on the ground.

'That's old *Pillans*!' somebody added in an angry shout.

'Comment?'

I pulled out of my knicker-leg the penny notebook and pencil that I now carried with me for the benefit of Madame's education and wrote in large letters 'Pillans'. Then I handed the book to her, said 'Yah!' very loudly and spat on the ground, whereupon word and gesture were repeated by all my companions.

'Pee long,' read Madame from the notebook. 'Pee long, yah, speet?'

'Yah!' we all shouted and spat again, Madame joining us, before we ran away round the corner to collapse into a helpless huddle of laughter while we sobbed out to one another Madame's name for the arch-enemy 'Pee long'.

Following the incident of the eel-swinger and Madame's purchase of the eel, I went into the eel-catching business but not for material gain. These days, with Doris and her officer friends giving me pennies every time they saw me, with the Belgie ladies paying me in food and cash for small services and horse droppings, with the sales of empty beer bottles that the soldiers left lying around and with the pennies earned by dancing and singing to the accompaniment of Sandy the Tinker and Tipperaray in the station yard, I was better fed and richer than I had ever been in my life. It has struck me since that I, unknown to my mother, spent more money in a week at this time on sweets, meat pies, penny notebooks and pencils, for which I had a mania, than she could save in a month with all her economy.

My mother came to know that children were obtaining money in various ways and sometimes she would say that this was vulgar but at other times she would ask me if I had been given any. Naturally, I told her I had not for I knew that if I confessed to having a penny, she would first slap me for being vulgar and then take the penny away from me to add to her economy. And then, one day after questioning me, she sighed and said: 'No. No free money would come *your* way, you useless feckless wee thing' and the subject was never mentioned again.

I did not go into the eel-catching business for money but for two other reasons. The first was that I liked Madame Fenchel, who liked eel soup and jellied eel, although how she could eat these things I did not understand. The second was that I had always regarded the eels as the serpents in the Paradise of Up-the-Burn. Compared with my fellows, I was not much of a killer. I did not catch butterflies because I preferred to watch them flying; I did not rob birds' nests and blow the eggs. I did not take fledgelings from nests and try to tame them until they died. I was not even interested in having frog spawn in a jam jar to turn into tadpoles, because you could watch them in all stages of this process in their native place in the swamp beside the Burn and my mother would not have tolerated tadpoles in our house in any case, any more than she would tolerate a bunch of wild flowers. Such things, in her eyes, were 'messy rubbish.' But eels, to me, were something quite different from any other form of life, except perhaps old Pillans. They were so sly, slimy, secretive, as they lay under the overhang of a boulder, coiled in a grey semi-circle as if they were part of it, until you came too near, when they would turn into strong steel snakes and go darting away, propelled by the nearly invisible fins that flickered along their slithery whiplash bodies. I loathed the eels and every time I killed one I felt a gloating joy that was an extreme of satisfaction, although hideous, because I had struck a blow against something even more hideous, something that was evil beyond all description.

Much as I liked to have pennies for sweets, meat pies, pencils and notebooks, I never charged Madame Fenchel anything for an eel although she gave me to understand that this was very foolish, but she was not aware, as I was aware, of how deeply immoral it would be to take money for ridding the world of an evil. I could not have explained this to her, for I could not explain it to myself, but I knew deeply and certainly that one might accept money for doing good, such as carrying Madame's letters to Belgium to the post office, but money might not be accepted for the eradication of evil. This was something one had to contribute to the world, free of charge. As I have said, I had early been accepted as the most ingenious and convincing liar in my school class. By the time I went into the eel-catching business, I was accepted as one of the best liars in the whole child tribe and I now became the champion eel-catcher, but this was not publicly known. It was a skill that I hugged secretly to my breast, my own secret war against evil and to talk of it or boast about it would have been in my mind what my mother called 'the very height of vulgarity,' something much more vulgar than Kingdom Come the Trammie shouting about God his father outside the pub door.

In the course of my many trips Up-the-Burn, I had developed an intimate knowledge of the Burn itself, having spent many hours wading in its clear water. I knew the pools where the eels were to be found, knew the favourite boulders round which they lay in curves invisible except to the practised eye and when, with one's loathing of them acting like armour, making of one an Iron Man, one had overcome one's revolt at their snaky slipperiness, had acquired the patience to squat motionless on a boulder in a pool and wait, the quick grab behind the gills, the quicker flick from water to bank and the killing blow on the head with a heavy stone were a mere matter of nimble skill.

The most difficult part of the entire operation was to convey the eel from the Burn to the Paddies but I found a simple way of overcoming this difficulty. Before an eel expedition, I found myself a stout paper bag from the Co-op dustbin and in my hole in the wash-house I had two pieces of strong string, one long and one short, known inside my head as my eel strings. Like all the girls of the gang, I was dressed from the skin out in a woollen semmit, then a hardish constricting garment called a 'liberty bodice,' then a pair of navy blue knickers with elastic at waist and knees, then a skirt that hung from a bodice topped by a woollen jersey.

So, having caught the eel, I coiled it inside the paper bag, tying the neck of the bag with my shorter string but with my longer string passed through a loop of it. The liberty bodice had several loops of tape at its bottom edge, from which other lengths of tape went to more tape loops at the top of one's woollen stockings in winter, to keep the stockings up so, when eel-catching, the long piece of string, with the eel bag hanging from it, went round my waist and through the loops so that under my skirt, I had a pouch of dead eel that was completely invisible.

After I became an eel-poacher, I seldom dropped over the Castle wall into the outside world again twice at the same spot, so that one time I would approach the Paddies from the Village, at another I would come from the direction of Loch-view Crescent, often meeting Beery-belly when heavy with eel and being passed by unsuspected. When carrying an eel, I boldly opened the gate of the Paddies, then the door and went in across the hall to the kitchen at the other side. If Madame was in her garden and I came in uninvited like this, she knew that I had an eel and followed me inside while, if she was not in the garden, she was in the kitchen already.

One day, after a successful trip Up-the-Burn, I came to the Paddies with a large eel in my dangling paper pouch but, although the weather was fine, Madame was not in the garden. When I went to the kitchen, she was not there either but only the younger lady called Antoinette. I pulled up my skirt, undid the string and let the eel bag fall to the stone floor. It burst and the horrible dead thing uncoiled itself slowly and evilly at my feet. If Antoinette had not been there, I should have run for my life but instead I looked up at her but she did not say a word in praise of the eel which was the biggest I had ever caught. She only looked up at the ceiling. Disappointed, I turned away. Madame Fenchel was always voluble in praise and gratitude when I brought her an eel and I should have liked to hear what she had to say about this yard of grey evil that was lying on the floor. I was just crossing the hall on my way out when Madame came rushing down the stone stairs, distraught as I had never seen her before, wringing her apron between her hands as she spoke rapidly to Antoinette in the kitchen doorway. Then, suddenly, she was speaking to me in a mixture of broken English and French, her voice becoming more and more shrill, her words more and more French as she held me by the shoulders and shook me in the effort to make me understand. In the end, she seized me by the wrist and ran, dragging me behind her, across the hall, up the stone stairs and into a room where one of the young Belgie ladies was lying on a bed, her body contorted, her grossly swollen belly heaving while she gave out dreadful gasping howls of agony. I understood. They needed the doctor.

'Aye! I'll get him!' I shouted and wrenching myself out of Madame's grip, I ran away as fast as I could up to the doctor's house. The maid said he was having lunch and would come afterwards, but I butted her in the stomach so that she fell backwards into a rack full of walking sticks and umbrellas while I barged into a room where I could hear voices and the sounds of cutlery.

'The Belgie lady down at the Paddies!' I shouted. 'You've got to come, you hear? You've got to come this minute!'

And he came. He went and got his black bag and he came but could I get the old pig to run? Oh, no. He walked along, quite fast it is true, but he would not run, him with his black hat and his gold watch-chain that dangled the seal ornaments over his fat belly. If he had not been the only doctor in Lochfoot, I would have nipped round behind him, tripped him and sent him sprawling into the gutter among the grey water and herring scales outside the fishmonger's shop.

When I reached the Paddies with him, chasing him ahead of me up the stone stairs, Madame Fenchel was amazed to see us—she thought that I had run away because I was frightened —and as the doctor went towards the bed, she burst into tears and clutched me to her big black bosom, hugging me and kissing me. It was not as pleasant as being kissed by Doris, for Madame smelled mostly of onions and her tears got themselves slobbered all over my face but it was wonderful to know that you had done something that helped people, had done quite a big bit of real good that made you know for sure, for once, that you were something other than a wee nuisance.

But the baby was born dead. Marie-Bernadette lived but after the baby came she wore black clothes all the time, like Madame Fenchel and Grammar. The baby had been all that she had had left of her husband who had been killed before she left Belgium. It was at this time that I discovered that it takes nine months for a woman to grow a baby inside her after she has done That with somebody and during that nine months, so much had happened to Marie-Bernadette. She had had to run away from her home because the Germans were coming and because Grammar could get money from a shipping office in Glasgow, the Belgie ladies had decided to run all the way from Belgium to Scotland and that was how they had landed, in the end, in Lochfoot.

I found all this out gradually from Madame, when she was crying over the flowers I brought for the baby's coffin. She said that the flowers were very beautiful but they were not so, in my opinion, although they were, as my mother would have said 'of the very best, like everything up at that Castle.' I made a special trip Up-the-Burn to pinch them and I do not mean that they were just wild roses either, although I put a big spray of wild roses with them to make them look a bit better.

In my explorations around the Castle, I had discovered that all the gardeners went home to their lodges for their dinner at eleven o'clock and that they never had one o'clock dinner like Railies and Trammies. So, the day after the baby was born dead, I went up there, waited till the gardeners had come out through the iron gate in the wall that surrounded the garden and then I ran right in there and into one of the big long glass-houses. I knew that the very best flowers were grown 'under glass,' for my mother often spoke of the 'chrysanths under glass' that had been grown at a house up Lochview. Under this Castle glass, there were hundreds of flowers, big fat red and yellow things in pots behind a board that said 'Begonias,' dangling purple and red bells in more pots behind a board that said 'Fuchsias' but all of them were hideous. If this was 'of the very best,' I would rather have wild roses, harebells and the marsh marigolds that grew beside the Burn at any time. I had gone to all this trouble, taken all this risk and there was not one thing in this whole rotten place that was in the least suitable to lay on a baby's coffin. But for the noise it would have made, I would have picked up a flower pot and have hurled it through the glass wall but I took up a cane and swept the heads off most of the fat begonias and the dangling fuchsias instead and then, down at the end of the house, I saw something that looked a bit better. There were a lot of bare stems hanging down from the wall, festooned with white waxy flowers that might have been a flight of white butterflies, so I took a grip on a rope-like stem and pulled. It was tough but, in the end it came, a long rope covered with sprays of white butterflies. I coiled it up, got out from my knickers the big brown paper bag from the Co-op dustbin, put the flowers inside, tied the bag round my waist with my eel strings and took myself off the way I had come.

On my way through the woodland, I picked a big spray of wild roses and in a thicket I had a look at the glass-house flowers. They were not too bad but the best thing about them was that when you coiled the rope stem into circles like this, they formed a natural wreath. I dropped out over the wall and carrying the spray of wild roses as camouflage in front of my bulgy skirt I made my way to the Paddies.

When Madame Fenchel made me understand that she wished to know where I had obtained such beautiful flowers, I made the traditional reply which was 'nowhere.' The flowers might be seen on the baby's coffin on the way to the cemetery but that did not matter. It was very unlikely that anybody who could recognize Castle orchids would look at the funeral of a Belgie baby and the Railies and Trammies who might cast a passing glance would not recognize an orchid any more than I had.

The baby died in the late spring of 1915 and although I had never seen it—only its little white coffin—I often remembered it, not as a coffin, but as a baby.

When we went back to school after the summer holidays and moved into a higher class, there was not much difference. In spite of the changes the war had made outside, school was much the same. There was still that old Bible stuff again every morning and the hymn one had to learn by heart was just a little more difficult, that was all. And not only did you have to learn the usual verse for every day for *this* new teacher expected you to answer questions about the hymn as well, in the name o' the Kingdom o' Heaven!

When from Egypt's house of bondage—

'Jean Robertson, where is Egypt? Colin Adair, do *you* know?' she asked, the old goat, as if anybody cared about all that old Bible stuff long ago.

Nevertheless, this teacher was quite determined that we would learn about Egypt and was not content that we should be able to repeat the words of our hymn and be done with it as all the other teachers had been. She made it all very interesting too and I began to feel that, if I were not careful, I would disgrace myself and begin to win prizes for school work, as if I were a Villager. It was all right for Villagers to win prizes but for a Railie like me it would never do. My life in the backyard of the Terrace would not be worth living.

Still, I could not help being interested in Egypt's house of bondage with its big stone beast called a Sphinx which was not unlike the iron lions that crouched outside the door of the Castle and its Pyramids which were big pointed heaps of bricks not unlike the tips down at the Gas Works. The people of Egypt had made slaves of the people of Israel—like in 'Britons never never will be slaves'—until this time that the hymn was about when Moses rose up and led the Israelites away from the house of bondage to the Promised Land. As the teacher told us about how they travelled across the miles and miles of desert, there came to birth in my mind a picture of a long straggle of people, a sinuous dark line like an eel snaking along the bed of the Burn while, from far above, the great stone beast looked down, as the Iron Man looked down from the mantelpiece in our kitchen. But this evil snaky line on the face of the desert was not an eel. It was made up of people, women carrying bundles, women leading toddlers by the hand, women trudging along, as the strange foreign-looking women, looking so frightened, had trudged away from the station on an October day behind old Joe's barrow.

In my chairbed one night, I thought how queer it was that something that had happened so long ago in the Bible that you could hardly believe that it had happened at all, should have happened again, right under your own very eyes. It was queer and it was very, very sad. It seemed that for ever and ever there had been serpents, like the one in the garden of Eden and the eels Up-the-Burn and that, for ever and ever, there had been beasts made of stone and men made of iron, these horrible circumstances of life that for ever oppressed people, imprisoning them in houses of bondage, until they ran away, from Egypt to the Promised Land, from Belgium to Lochfoot and from Lochfoot up Lochview or to the war.

Looking up at the Iron Man above my head, I began to cry quietly and secretly because of all the circumstances and because the Belgie baby was dead. I would never now be able to catch it a special small eel, as a present, all for itself.

CHAPTER SEVEN

Time, like an ever-rolling stream,
Bears all its sons away;
They fly forgotten, as a dream
Dies at the opening day.

HYMN 601

BUSY AS I WAS with all my extra war-time activities, I did not let them absorb my entire attention. It was just conceivable that the war might end one day, so that one would have to return to one's former circumstances and it seemed to me, therefore, to be essential to maintain contact with this other way of life. I continued with my secret sinful reading, I rang a few doorbells on dark winter evenings, I gave a little time to wee Sammy Gardiner, taking him to visit the Belgies and Doris and once or twice to visit my granny in the Village. I did not let any week pass without spending a few hours with my granny.

During these visits, I told her of some of my doings but not of others. I told her about our dancing and singing in the station yard; I told her about Madame Fenchel and the Belgies but I did not tell her about my friendship with Doris and the ladies at the Arms or that I caught eels Up-the-Burn for the Belgies. The reason why I held these reservations from my granny was perfectly clear in my mind although, at the time, I should have been hard pressed to put it into words. It was that I knew my granny would have felt compelled to disapprove of Doris and to disapprove of my poaching eels, for poaching was a form of stealing, much worse than mere pinching and it would have made my granny unhappy to have had to disapprove of anything connected with me. She would not have scolded or slapped me, as my mother would have done but she would be sad with disapproval and

I did not want to make my granny sad. I was taking risks in being friends with Doris and in poaching eels. The big girls said that you could go to Hell for speaking to a whore like Doris and you could certainly go to prison for poaching, for this often happened to the Tinkers who were caught doing it, but I did not wish my granny to be involved in any of my personal risks. We always had plenty to talk about without touching upon Doris or eels.

My granny, for instance, liked to hear about school and the Village being so different in every way from the Terrace, you could talk about school inside Lilac Cottage without anybody thinking you were a softie.

'Colin Adair is Leader now, since David went off to the Academy,' I told my granny.

'They are a clever lot the Adairs,' she said. 'Is Colin good at his lessons as well as at fighting in the playground?'

'He is good at *everything*!' I said enthusiastically.

I would never have said such a thing or have shown such enthusiasm to any of my fellows of the playground—it would have led to writing about Colin and me on the wall in that dirty place behind the water closets—but in my granny's house I could air a little of my devotion and gratitude to the Adairs.

Isabel, who had championed me in those far-off days when I was very young, had left me as a legacy for playground protection to her brother David and when he departed to the Academy, he had left me in turn to Colin. Their championship of me was, of course, an undeclared thing, something even, almost disconnected from myself as a person. To protect wee Jeanie Robertson was simply something that the Adairs *did*, in the way that they grew taller and more robust than most other children and were always top of their class. And their protection of me was not a demonstrative thing. It was simply that, as soon as I was in difficulty, there would come the authoritative voice of Colin.

'Telfer, let her alone or I'll bash your teeth in' and to me: 'Get away out of it, you cheeky wee smout!'

'We have a new thing at school now, Granny,' I told her one day.

'What's that?'

'Drill. Every Wednesday, the drill teacher comes at twelve o'clock and we get out into the playground and we march round and round and touch our toes and do knees bend and then we have a game.'

'A game?' she repeated with wonder.

'Aye. It's great. There's a game called Bean Bags—that's our favourite.'

'Bean Bags? I never heard o' bairns playin' at the school but them in charge knows best, likely.'

This was one of the differences between my granny and my mother or Miss Miller. My mother said that drill and games was a lot of nonsense and a waste of time while Miss Miller said Bean Bags was a scandalous waste of public money but my granny was always willing to concede that somebody might know more about things like education than she did. My granny, of course, had never claimed to know what was what. This was one of the things that made her so comfortable to be with.

One wet Saturday afternoon, I was down at Lilac Cottage when somebody knocked at the front door.

'Now, who will that be?' my granny asked. 'If it's Donnie Mackinlay bringing the spade back, tell him to put it round in the shed.'

But it was not old Donnie Mackinlay with the spade. It was the postman with his brown canvas bag on his shoulder and he handed me a soiled white card. I was so astonished that I stood gaping at him as he let himself out of the gate, the card quivering in my hand. It was the first time that I had ever opened a door to find the postman on the other side, for my life was one in which communication consisted in the main of a few standard formulae, in which to find words for anything unusual was of supreme difficulty and in which written communication did not exist at all, except in cases of extreme nature and urgency, as when I had written 'Pillans' in my notebook for Madame Fenchel.

'Who is it, Jean?' my granny called from the fireside.

'The—the postman?' I said, finding my voice with difficulty.

'Come on then! Hurry up! What did he bring?'

Her voice had an impatience that I had never before heard in it, an impatience that made me look down at the card that I held. On it was written, in a straggly hand that would have earned the writer the strap in my class at school: 'Mrs. Robertson, Lilac Cottage, Lochfoot Village, by Glasgow, Scotland.'

I carried it to my granny who turned it over and read what was on the other side and then, with her eyes all soft with tears, she looked up at me and said: 'They can all say what they like, Jean, but Hugh—your father—is a good man.'

When she spoke the words 'They can all say what they like,' my mind filled with a crowded, composite smudgy picture of the Iron Man on the mantel at home, the great stone snake of the Castle wall as seen from the hilltop and my mother and Miss Miller gossiping disapprovingly at the close mouth while I heard again the long wail of the whistle as the train went snaking into the black hole of the tunnel.

'That,' I said, pointing to the card, 'is from—from my father?'

'Aye.' She handed the card to me and, holding it, I began to remember him, first as a shambling drink-sodden shadow, shuffling along in unlaced boots round the corner of the Terrace but then, more clearly, as a younger square-shouldered man in his blue serge Sunday suit, who held my hand as we walked side by side down the road from Railway Terrace to the Village, going to visit my granny on a Sunday afternoon. I looked down at the card. 'Dear Mother,' I read, 'I am fine. I hope you are the same Yours truly Hugh.'

'He is all right,' I said after a moment, as I realized that these words had been written by the living hand of my father who had, until today, been so shadowy in my memory that he had had no more substance than the remembered dying wail of the train.

'Aye,' my granny said. 'Go an' make a cup 'o tea, lassie.' Over the tea, she was silent at first as she looked into the flames of her fire but as I poured out a second cup for her, she said: 'Maybe ye don't know it, Jean lassie, but I am not truly your granny.'

As if I did not know it! Had not my mother made this point often enough? But I said nothing and waited.

'I wasna your father's mother, Jean. I married your grandfather shortly after his first wife died, when your father was a baby.' She paused for a long time before she added thoughtfully: 'Of course, it all depends what you mean by a mother. I was as fond 'o wee Hugh as if he was my own.'

'And you are *so* my granny!' I said with emphasis, then added with difficulty as I tried to say the impossible '*Inside* me, you're my granny!'

She smiled at me a little and looked back into the fire, her hands folded over the card which lay in the lap of her apron. I had a sudden feeling that she would like to be alone with her card and her fire in the home that had been hers for so long and I wanted to be alone too, that I might reconstruct in my mind this man who had come back from the dead.

'I have to go now, Granny,' I said and fetched my old coat from the hook behind the door.

'All right, Jean.' As I buttoned the coat, she turned her head to look at me. 'Jean, has your mother ever heard from him?'

'No. I don't think so.'

'Then ye'll not tell her about this?' She looked from me

down to the card. 'This is the fifth time he's written to me, the good lad, for it's not easy for him. But I wouldna like your mother—I wouldna like her to be, well, hurt, like, Jean.'

'I won't tell her,' I said brusquely and let myself out into the rain, without giving my granny my opinion that if my mother did hear about the card, she would not be hurt. She would probably be very angry but that was very different.

When I was in my chairbed that night, that moment when I held the card in my hand and remembered my faraway young father in his Sunday suit came back to me and it was followed by other memories, as if the card were a secret pass into a long-forgotten world. I remembered how, once, my father used to sit on the wooden chair on the other side of the empty grate from where I now lay. His legs were crossed and I sat astride his foot while he held my hands and kicked his foot up and down, making with his tongue all the time the clip-clop noise of a horse walking along a road. At this moment, my mother, who was sewing in the candlelight with her back to my bed, made an irritable noise at a knot in her thread and I remembered that she stopped the horse-riding game because the blacking from his boot soiled my knickers.

Looking up at the Iron Man on the mantel, I next remembered the first serious quarrel between my father and my mother, or perhaps it was merely the first that stamped itself on my memory.

It took place when my mother announced that she had enough money saved to buy a mangle. I had not gone to school as yet, but I knew about mangles. Old Mrs. Gurney had a mangle and 'took in mangling' which meant that people took their newly washed sheets to her and she put them through between the heavy rollers of the mangle by turning the big iron wheel, so that the sheets came out at the other side, all folded and smooth. Mrs. Gurney charged people twopence to do their mangling but it saved a lot of ironing. My mother had never paid any twopences to Mrs. Gurney but it appeared now that she was going to save the ironing by having a mangle of her own.

This was not, however, my mother's idea. What she intended to do was not only her own mangling but the mangling of other people for doing which she intended to charge twopence, like Mrs. Gurney. The argument began, the voices grew louder and angrier and it culminated in my father's saying: 'Bring a mangle in here an' you'll be a widow like old Jenny Gurney, for the minute a mangle comes into this house, I go out of it.'

The mangle did not come into the house but, now, as I thought of that far off time and the time that came after, it struck me that it might have been better for my father if the mangle had come into the house and he had gone out of it. But my father had stayed and an iron as relentless as the iron rollers of the mangle had closed about him until he turned into the slovenly Saturday-night drunk who slept it off all day Sunday of my clear memory. His boots, had he swung me on his foot at this later time, would not have soiled my knickers with their blacking for he did not clean his boots any more. And he and I no longer went for walks. He drew away into a brick brown darkness, slaving out his weeks in the railway siding, getting drunk at the weekends and skulked and slouched off back to work on Monday mornings, scarcely more solid than his own faint shadow on the grimy brick wall.

One evening in the late autumn of 1917, my mother and I were sitting at table, having our supper, the last meal of the day, which meant that the time was about six o'clock. The meal was, as on every evening, boiled potatoes, a slice of bread spread with margarine, tea with skimmed milk and no sugar. The wartime scarcity of sugar that caused it to be rationed gave my mother a patriotic excuse to buy none at all. Suddenly, there was a tramp-tramp of heavy boots along the close, the door opened and my father stood there. He was not the man I remembered at all. His face had colour in it and his clothes were so strange. A khaki cape hung over one shoulder above a dirty khaki tunic and he wore a kilt which was covered with a sort of over-skirt of khaki cloth. His legs, from ankle to knee, were wrapped in khaki puttees and over the shoulder that was free of the cape he had a khaki kitbag with a steel helmet attached to it by its chin strap. I had seen hundreds of men dressed like this but on my father the clothes looked very strange and at the same time made a stranger out of him. He smiled at me and said: 'You're no' very big but ye're a bonnie lass, Jean' before he looked at my mother and threw a parcel on to the table. 'Pork chops,' he said. 'Fry the lot. I'm starving.'

I remember the pork chops—never had there been such a meal at Number Three Railway Terrace—I remember the silence and most of all do I remember my pity for my mother. She looked so frightened, as if this silent authoritative man at the table was a stranger returned from the dead—not her husband, not any man she had ever known but yet risen from the dead, a stranger who had come unbidden into the house which, for three years had been so much her own, and had ordered her to cook this vulgarly extravagant meal for him. I think, now, that this estimate of how my mother felt may have been fairly accurate. She was a self-sufficient person who made no demands for affection and gave no affection so that, when my father went to the war, she did not miss him except in material ways. She therefore missed him with relief more than anything. There were no longer his dirty working clothes to be washed, less money needed to be spent on food and her time was all her own for the carrying through of the small economies from which she derived her greatest satisfaction in life. Before my father had gone to the war, she had been able to ignore and despise him as a drunken shiftless waster and in her memory, the waster had faded to a faint wraith as, in my own memory, he had been for years no more than the dying wail of the train whistle but it was impossible to ignore or despise this straight-eyed keen-jawed man who, having eaten his pork chops, pushed back his chair from the table and lit a cigarette.

Not looking at him, my mother rose from the table and took up the kettle of hot water that would wash the dishes. Moving round behind him, from gas-ring to sink, she glanced sidewise at the back of his head and I heard her draw a sharp breath and then she stood there as if suddenly turned to stone. When she spoke, all her fear of the stranger, all her resentment at this interference in her planned, settled unencumbered life and all her hatred of dirt and 'vulgarity' were in her voice as she said in a near scream of loathing: 'Hughie Robertson, you're alive! For God's sake, get out of this house!'

To those unversed in Lochfoot dialect and idiom, the words 'you're alive' may seem strange but they merely made me look at the back of my father's head to which my mother's horrified eyes were riveted. He was certainly 'alive', I observed with interest. He was 'alive' in a degree that, in my considerable experience of this form of 'aliveness', I had never seen before. The lice in his hair and on the collar of his khaki tunic were so numerous that hair and khaki seemed to be in constant movement.

'Get out of here this minute!' my mother screamed. 'Get out before you have the whole place polluted!'

I rose from the table, staring at her, frightened. I had seen her angry many times but I had never seen her eyes as wild as this and the complexity of what she was feeling had not as yet come home to me. My father was looking up at her calmly, his eyes almost smiling through the smoke of the cigarette that hung from the corner of his mouth.

'Da,' I said in a low voice, 'come on.'

'Where to, Jean?' he asked quietly.

'Out to the wash-house, with *me*.'

'All right.'

He stood up and looked at my mother for a second, but he did not speak to her, before he followed me out of the house. I do not think that he ever spoke to her again.

Out in the wash-house, my father took command. At his instructions, I filled the boiler with water, lit the fire under it and then went into the house to take the yellow soap from the sink and the towel from the nail. Later on, after he had bathed himself in the round wooden tub and I had washed his shirt and underwear and had boiled them in the boiler, I went into the house again and took two candles from the cupboard. I had never before dared to open the cupboard door but my mother, sitting by the empty grate, watched what I took each time I went in but she did not speak except when she pointed to the kitbag and said: 'Take that out with you.' I did as she told me, dragging the bag behind me, leaving her alone in the kitchen under the Iron Man and in and out from wash-house to house I went until my father was dressed in the Sunday suit that had come home in a brown paper parcel over three years ago, when he had gone to the war.

Then, by the light of the candles, he and I began to clean the lice out of the pleats of the tartan kilt. I had washed the cape, tunic and socks, had boiled the rest of his clothing but, as he said, the kilt was a real bugger. It could not be washed but had to be cleaned by hand. He showed me how to open the pleats of tartan, get my thumb nail into the fold and push downwards from top to bottom so that the khaki shower fell into the tub of soapy water on the floor between us. With every shower, he and I became merrier and merrier. It was a task from which I derived tremendous satisfaction, a similar hideous satisfaction to that which came from killing eels but it took us three evenings from my coming home from school until bedtime to clean the kilt completely. Each evening, having done our stint, my father would go out somewhere and I would hang the kilt out on the clothes line until the next evening.

While my father was in the house, my mother did not speak a word but, in his absence, she tried to release some of her pent-up feeling. The kilt, swinging a little in the grey October air of the backyard, became a fixation with her. In her eyes, it declared my father's filth to the whole world and she would have liked to remove it from the clothes-line but she did not dare. In another way, I was equally obsessed by the kilt, so that before I went to school in the morning, I would inspect it, opening a few pleats to see if anything still moved there and I would repeat the process when I came home at dinner-time. I was determined that, by the time my father had to don that kilt again, not one hated persistent louse would be lingering in its complicated folds and each time I came into the house and my father was not present, which was frequent, my mother would scream: 'Ye vulgar brat! Can't ye leave that thing alone? What'll folk think? I've never been so disgraced in a' my life—you out there pickin' lice in front o' the whole Terrace!'

On the third day, at dinner-time, she lost all control of herself and struck me so hard that I fell into the empty fire-place and, as I struggled to my feet, I said: 'If you hit me again, I'll tell my da.'

For a moment, she stared at me like a terrified animal, then threw herself on to the bed and began not to cry but to shudder, her whole body heaving with some terrible thing inside her that struggled to come out but could not. She made me think of Marie-Bernadette on the bed at the Paddies that day when the baby was born dead. In the moment when she had struck me, I had hated her but now, as she lay there, I was filled with a terrible pity.

'Don't, Ma,' I said. 'Come and eat your dinner,' and after a moment she came to sit opposite to me at the table.

That was the last time that my mother struck me and not only during the little time that my father was at home. She did not ever raise a hand against me again.

My father was not at home very much in the sense of being in our house. I knew that he went to see my granny each day but where he went for the rest of the time I did not know, but I knew that he did not get drunk. I have since come to suspect that he passed his time with the men at the Castle Home Farm where he used to work so long ago. He was at home in all for a little over a week and then there came a morning when, as we sat eating porridge and skimmed milk before I left for school, I felt that, at any moment, somebody might shout 'Up Lochview!' and there would be nothing in the world but an orgy of destruction that would die away into the wailing of a train whistle.

My father came out to the close mouth with me and there he put his hand on my shoulder and said: 'You are a good wee lass and a bonnie wee lass, Jean. Watch out for the laddies, mind!'

He would then have turned away from me but I said: 'What train are you going by, Da?'

'Never mind that. You are to go to the school, Jean,' he said, trying to be stern as he looked down at me. 'The school will stand by you——'

'I'm going to the school, Da,' I assured him. 'What train?'

'The one o'clock.'

I ran away to school. It was a Wednesday and at forenoon interval I found Colin Adair in the playground.

'Colin, listen——'

'Listen what? I'm busy.'

'Colin, my da is going back to the war on the one o'clock train. I want to go to the station.'

'Jeanie Robertson, are you going to plunk?'

'Plunking' or playing truant was a crime that no Villager would countenance as a rule.

139

'Only quarter o' an hour, Colin. At Bean Bags, could you an' Jessie—' Jessie Miller was the girl leader of the time '—could ye work the game across to the gates?'

'You'll never get out! Old Drillie'll see you!'

'Will you work the game across to the gates?'

'All right. I'll see what Jessie says.'

With this I had to be content but when the game of Bean Bags began, it was unusually fast and furious until a violent scuffle was raging close to the gates which pushed them open about six inches, as far as their linking chain and padlock would allow. It was enough. On my side, I edged through, while the covering scuffle and shouting went on and was away at a crouching run under the concealing wall down to Pillans's corner.

Straightening up, I took the turn at full tilt down to the Village where, a few yards ahead, I saw my father coming out of the gate of Lilac Cottage, his kitbag with the attached helmet on his shoulder, his clean kilt swinging as he strode along.

I ran quietly up behind him and put my hand into his, the first time that I had really touched him since the Sundays long ago when he used to take me walking down to the Village to see my granny. We walked together to the station but I do not remember that we spoke until the train door was shut between him and me and the iron snake began to move.

'You are a good lass, Jean,' he said then. 'Ta-ta!'

'Ta-ta, Da,' I said and turned away.

It was in April of 1918 that the telegram came to Number Three Railway Terrace to announce that he had been killed but the slip of paper had no real meaning. My father had been dead to this address ever since that evening of the pork chop supper when my mother had screamed: 'You're alive!' and he and I had gone out to the wash-house. Death comes in strange ways and with unlikely words, sometimes and is not always, even in war, the work of an artillery barrage or a sniper's bullet.

My mother wept over the telegram, of course, for it would be vulgar to do any less. Maybe that is cruel, but let it stand. My mother wept and Miss Miller and the neighbours proffered sympathy but not very much. Sympathy, at this stage in the war, was growing scarce, like sugar, for most of the reserves had already been used up.

On the evening of the telegram, I went down to tell my granny what had happened and when I opened the door and went in, she looked round at me from her little low chair by the fire before I could speak and said: 'So my Hugh laddie is gone, is he?' She turned away from me and looked back into her fire. 'He was a wee fair chap, just a year old. But for wee Hugh needing a mother, I believe I would have died an old maid instead o' an old man's darlin'.' She sighed, dismissing her little joke which was her tribute to the memory of my father.

'Och, well, what is to be will be. Make us a cup o' tea, Jean, there's a good lass.'

I made the tea and while she drank it she sat silent while I thought how, in all Lochfoot, my granny and my father were the only people who called me 'Jean' and not 'Jeanie'. It marked in a comforting way my special relationship with them.

My granny did not cry about my father being killed but she talked to me more that night than she had ever talked before. I do not mean to convey that she was a sullen or bad-tempered woman for this was not so but she was neither gay like Doris, volatile like Madame Fenchel nor censorious like Miss Miller. She was a peaceful silent woman, with a curious inner repose and always sat quietly by her fire when I called on her, giving me the pleasure of doing little things for her without interference. She was much liked and respected in the Village and friendly with all her neighbours, relied upon for help in cases of sickness and the little services that she rendered were repaid in kind, in the way that the Adair boys chopped her firewood and the man from Ivy Cottage did the heavy digging of her garden.

Sometimes, when I went to see her, she did not even greet me in words but with a little welcoming smile and gesture and sometimes she would not speak all the time I was with her, except when I was leaving, when she would say: 'Come down again when you get the chance, Jean, lass.' On this evening, however, after she had had her first cup of tea, she began to talk at length for the first time about the past and I learned that my father had been a late baby, twelve years younger than his youngest sister and the only boy in the family of five. My real grandmother had died at his birth and my granny had married my grandfather, a man thirty-five years older than herself, when my father was 'a wee fair chap, just a year old.' My granny did not know where the four sisters, my aunts were or whether they were alive or dead. They had all gone to service in 'London and America and places' and had stopped writing. They had never been 'great hands at the writing anyway', any more than my granny herself had been.

'It was a pity that they lost touch with home, maybe,' she said, 'but why should they write to *me*? Even Martha, the youngest one, was off into service at the Castle as soon as your grandfather and I were married. They owe nothing to *me*, poor lassies.'

She now retired into her silence again, gazed into her fire for a long time before she said: 'And you owe me nothing either, Jean. I've never given you anything but your name and it was your father that called you after me. But you are welcome here any time you like to come, only I don't want to make trouble between you and your mother, for that would not be right. I could wish that things were different but folk are according to their natures.' Never did she speak a word of direct criticism of my mother but her attempts to conceal her dislike spoke more loudly than any words.

As I was leaving her that night, she looked up at me and said: 'I am not howling and running to the neighbours for sympathy about your father being gone, Jean, but that doesna mean that I am not sorry. Yet things could have been worse. I would rather know he was dead than have him home here with no legs, sitting in a chair like Gardiner the Cobbler. Some folk get it real hard, as if one lameter in a family wasna enough but the Gardiners manage real well in spite of everything.'

On my way home, it came to me that the Gardiner's house was the only one that my granny visited outside of the Village. The cobbler's shop was a little hole in the wall between the Co-op and the butcher's and each morning, on my way to school, I could look in and see Mr. Gardiner, sitting in his wheelchair and hammering away at the boots he was mending. I had never thought, until now, that the war had brought not one lameter but two into the Gardiner family and I made a mental note that, as soon as I had a spare moment, I must take wee Sammy for an outing again, down to see Doris or Madame or to the station to watch the trains.

After my father was killed, I felt even more in it with my granny than before but my attitude to my mother changed completely. Hitherto, I had been afraid of her, not only of her anger and her slaps and her complete control of the physical aspect of my life. More than I had been afraid of these things, I had been afraid of the rigidity in her, her cold certainty of her knowledge of what was what.

Now, when I remembered that evening of the pork chops, it came to me that my mother had not been afraid of my father but of how he had made her see herself. My father had not made her afraid of himself but, as he sat there in his reality and integrity, his own man who had thrown off the frustrations, the iron fetters of this house and the sub-life that she had imposed upon it, he had made her see for a few terrifying moments her own hollowness. He had made her see that she was not a woman in the way that he was a man. He had made her see that she was only a shell and no more a human being than the Iron Man on the mantel and it was this knowledge, naked before her mind for a few moments, that had made her so suddenly and terribly afraid. She could not bear his presence, his reality, as he had exposed himself to her that evening, so that she had had to get him out of her sight. The lice that had crawled on him were only an excuse. And he, as if he had given her one last chance to be human and not a hollow shell, drew away from her finally in that moment when he followed me out to the wash-house. Clean, dressed in his Sunday suit, he had come and gone during the few days of his leave, never speaking to her, almost unaware of her presence, as if he had decided that communication with her was as impossible as it would be with the Iron Man that looked down on us.

As soon as he had gone back to France, she had put all thought of him behind her, had settled back into the rigid routine of her days, re-building round herself her protection from all the realities of human contact, those 'vulgarities' and 'extravagances' which were the failings of those who did not know what was what. As I watched her scrape the margarine on to the bread and count over, on Saturday night, when she thought I was safely asleep, the few pennies she had saved during the week, I hated and despised her but then I would remember those few moments over the bones of the pork chops, when she had been so mortally afraid and I would feel for her only a heart-rending pity. If only, I wished, it were possible to make her see that happiness lay more in the cleaning of the lice out of the pleats of a kilt than in counting pennies, she need never feel that fear that had gripped her again. But I knew that she would never see this now. She was as she was and she would not change. Vaguely I was aware that what she was was not entirely her own

144

fault. She had been conditioned by circumstances to believe that to be 'in good circumstances' was the most desirable consummation of life and she was still practising the economy she had always practised towards that end. I began to see her as the pathetic docile product of the lower stratum of a society that believed in nothing as intensely as it believed in the power of wealth, a society so blinded by the light reflected off gold that it could see neither the earth nor the stars. She prided herself on being a 'woman of character who knew her own mind' but at this time I came to see that she had little character and less mind. She was a standard product of her time, the turn of the nineteenth and twentieth centuries and also a standard product of her place, the brick walls and iron railings of Lochfoot. She was a mass-produced casting like the Iron Man on the mantel but it was not her fault. She was the product of circumstances and it was in this that my sadness and my pity for her lay.

As I watched her count her pennies, I had a vague unformulated knowledge that her very economy that was to lead her to better circumstances had itself built up into a circumstance, high as the Castle wall, that was barring her out for ever from life as it was known to my granny and me and as it had been known to my father. While, at some times, I thought these things about my mother in a groping way in the dimness of my mind, at other times I would think that she was quite right in the way she lived and thought and that I myself simply had 'no sense', as she often told me. Certainly, it must be pleasant to be rich enough to live at the Castle or in Lochview Crescent or even up Victoria Drive but when I went Up-the-Burn, I never saw any Castle people enjoying the Dam and the woods as I did, when I took a stroll up Lochview, the cream blinds were always drawn down over the windows in the afternoon silence and up Victoria Drive, all the people were old and looked too tired to enjoy anything. Then I would think that maybe it was a good thing that my father had been killed, that the man who came in with the parcel of pork chops that evening would never know of that final circumstance of life, being too old to enjoy anything. And now, of course, I would remember again how afraid my mother had been for those few moments and I would feel sorry for her all over again and wish that I could help her. It was an endless tortuous snake of thinking, like following the Castle wall and always coming back to your starting point so that, my patience at an end, if it were daytime, I would go to visit my granny or Doris or, if I were on my chairbed, I would begin to sing my current hymn inside my head. One evening, about a month after my father was killed, I came home from the Village to be greeted with the words: 'Where have *you* been? Down in that hovel in the Village again? From now on, you'll spend more time at home, my lady. There's work to be done,' whereupon my mother threw open the door to our empty parlour, but it was no longer as empty as it had been. On the mantelshelf, there stood a new oil lamp or, rather, a secondhand oil lamp that was new to our house and in the middle of the floor there stood a mangle, its iron stand, its big iron wheel and handle, the curve of iron over the top of the rollers throwing a grotesque shadow on the wall. I could hardly bear to look at the iron monster itself for that very shadow on the wall seemed to symbolize all the iron bars, the cramping restrictions of the life in Lochfoot that had made my father grateful for the release to the mud, lice and blood of Flanders but, while I stared in horror, my mother became more and more animated, her eyes sparkling as she visualized the twopences dropping into her ready palm. She began to turn the handle and the machine began to clank-clank-clank.

In the centre of the curve of metal that extended from one upright to the other above the rollers, there was a thick adjusting screw. On Mrs. Gurney's mangle, this was topped by an iron wheel, perhaps three inches in diameter, which was turned to make the adjustment, but on this later more refined mangle that my mother had acquired, there was no little wheel. Instead, there was a black-lacquered, crudely-cast helmeted head, the visor closed and under this, on the metal curve was written in gilt lettering on black lacquer the words: 'Knight's Triple Action Mangle'. During a second of blind panic, I felt that our house was being invaded by Iron Men and not only our house for, as my mother made the machine clank-clank, I could hear them tramping through all the streets of Lochfoot, tramping over the whole world and as they passed they left behind them a dingy desert of brick walls and iron posts and concrete, as if the backyard of Railway Terrace had widened its boundaries to cover all the green earth. And in the same panic-stricken second I realized that the terror of the Iron Men was that they were faceless, that eyes, nose and mouth were hidden behind the iron masks but what was even more frightening was my knowledge that, if the masks were lifted, the faces underneath would look as my mother's face looked as she clank-clanked with the iron handle, hard-eyed and pinched with greed as she visualized the twopences to be gained. Staring as if mesmerized at the turning rollers, she had forgotten me and I ran out of the house and locked myself in the water closet. While I sat there in the dank smelly greyness with the squares of newspaper dangling from their nail on the wall, it came to me that not the least sinister feature of the clanking monster was that it had come from old Pillans's Secondhand. It was big enough too and, unlike the bookcase and the books, worth enough money to have been caressed, probably, by his thin snaky hands that left behind them, I was sure, a trail of slime.

The human race, however, is noted for its adaptability. People can become inured to anything and panics like passions were short-lived in the day-to-day atmosphere of

Railway Terrace. Only the lower belly-crawling vices, like the love of money, seemed to thrive in that thin bleak air. I began to help my mother with the mangling but only as seldom as I could and I helped her at all only because, sometimes, pity for her overcame me.

There was something infinitely pathetic in her belief that God would be pleased with her for working so hard and collecting all these twopences. She charged twopence for a certain quantity of work and an extra penny to deliver the finished mangling to its owner and she was more than astonished when I made the first delivery, came home and handed her twopence.

'Where's the delivery money?' she asked.

'I've got it. I did the delivering. It's mine.'

We had a long argument but I would not hand over the penny and in the end, she had to agree that if I delivered a bundle, I retained the fee and I came to the knowledge that she respected me for this stand, seeing in me, she thought, something of her own love for what she called 'an honest penny'.

I made the stand, however, not for the penny but for a principle, the principle that she might have held my father down in an iron grip for several years but that she was never going to exert such a grip over myself. Had she but known it, I could have spent a pleasant afternoon up at the Dam, guddling for trout, which I could have sold to the ladies at the Arms for twenty times her mangling delivery fee.

It was at about this time that I discovered the purpose of the second locked kist in our kitchen. Enclosed within herself as my mother was, I do not think that she realized that I was growing up and although I was now a twelve-year-old graduate of a very tough, wily and lawless school, she often still addressed me as 'ye silly wee thing'. We spoke to one another little and then only to argue, as a rule and when I came in from my evening activities, I usually undressed at once, turned down my chairbed and pretended to fall asleep right away. One Saturday night, she too undressed but with the candle still alight and although I had been on the verge of sleep, this breach in the economy alerted me. In her nightgown, she moved the candle from the table to the floor, then opened the damp smelly cupboard underneath the sink and took out from under a rotten floorboard a key. Kneeling on the floor, as if before an altar, she removed the turkey red cotton cover, put the key in the lock and raised the lid of the kist. Quietly, she lifted up one little paper bag of coins and laid it back in place with a tiny chinking sound, then another and then another. Having conned over the bags one by one, she picked out a roll of notes and held it between her hands for a moment before replacing it and extracting her purse from the pocket of her skirt which lay upon a chair. She then counted coins out of the purse into another paper bag, put this in the kist and with a long satisfied sigh closed down the lid. When she had locked the kist, replaced the red cover and hidden the key under the sink, she blew out the candle and I heard her get into bed.

On several occasions after this, I thought of opening the kist, at some time when she was out on a mangling delivery, to see how much money was in it or even to pinch some of it, in order to find out how she would react to her loss but I could never bring myself to take the key from under the rotten floorboard. The Iron Man was on one side of the room, the kist on the other and I felt that if I took one of these coins in my hand, I might be linked through it to the Iron Man and become for ever a part of some chain of evil.

Throughout the summer of 1918, I pursued my customary avocations, visiting my granny, Doris and the Belgies, marauding with the child tribe and helping my mother a little with the mangling on Sundays.

Our Sunday work did not go on for long, however. As I have mentioned, the mangle made a clank-clanking noise

149

and on about the third or fourth Sunday we operated it, Miss Miller 'knocked through' to us. 'Knocking through' or 'knocking up' or 'knocking down' was a feature of life in Railway Terrace and Tramway Buildings. The walls between apartments were thin, there was no insulation between ceilings below and floors above and almost every Saturday night my mother used to have to knock up to Mrs. Anderson because Mr. Anderson, before he was killed at the war, was, unlike my father, a very noisy drunk. He would come thumping from wall to wall in through the close, go bang-banging up the stone stairs, there would be the thud of his house door shutting and then two more thuds as he took off his heavy boots and threw them across the room against the opposite wall. It was at this point that my mother would take the broom from the corner and, holding it by the bristle head, reach up and knock with the end of the handle against our ceiling. Down the years, she had created a little range of hills and valleys in the ceiling above our sink.

Until the Sunday when we were operating the mangle, nobody had ever knocked through or down to us before and my mother was indignant at Miss Miller's doing so now, although she was well aware that knocking up to the Fergusons above her was one of Miss Miller's main pastimes. Miss Miller, it was said, was the sort that knocked up if you dropped a pin. But the noise of our mangle was more than a pinfall and although our kitchen was separated from Miss Miller's by the three feet of the close, the two parlours were separated by only a thin wall. It was part of Miss Miller's uppishness that she sat in her parlour on Sunday afternoons, going to the extravagance of lighting a fire in it, if you please and when the knock-knock came on the wall as we were folding a newly mangled sheet, my mother could hardly believe her own ears.

'She's knocking through!' she said. 'The uppish bizzom! The vulgarity of it!'

Nevertheless, we did no more mangling on Sundays. The discontinuance of a noise that had caused a knocking-up, down or through was a primitive law that was obeyed as faithfully by the adults as the law forbidding clyping was obeyed by us of the child tribe.

One grey day, we all came home from school at dinner-time and as we came up past the shops, we saw something very strange. There was a Union Jack hanging over the door of the Co-op and various flags sticking out of the house windows above. When we came round the corner to Railway Terrace, there was a flag—in some cases more than one—hanging out of every window except ours and then the cry rose out of the ground that the war was finished. The war was finished, the Germans were beaten and *we* had won! In a shouting mob, we all went rushing along past the Terrace, round the corner and along past the flags on the façade of Tramway Buildings, banged into the Castle wall at the end and came rushing back. Then, at the corner of the Buildings and the Terrace, we all suddenly halted. There was a grey drizzle of rain, the flags hung limp and dreary on the grimy brick walls and the excitement ebbed out of us like a sad tide leaving a sadder shore. We all scattered and went to our homes for dinner.

'The war's finished,' I told my mother. 'You should have a flag out.' It did not matter to me that our parlour window did not have a flag like all the others in the Terrace. If you share a house with someone, it is necessary to communicate and between my mother and myself, the only communication was mutual criticism. She criticized me for being dirty, stupid, useless and a variety of other things and I criticized her whenever the opportunity presented itself. Conformity was a law of life in the Terrace. If Miss Miller and the people upstairs had flags out and they had, we ought to have a flag out also but this time my mother was not prepared to conform to the tribal law.

'You hold your tongue,' she told me. 'I have more to do with my money than buy flags and rubbish.'

We then had our dinner in silence. The need to communicate had been served.

From my point of view, the ending of the war was harmful rather than beneficial, as I had long suspected that it might be, for the day came when Doris and all her lovely friends went away, not temporarily in a Black Maria this time, but for good, forewarning us of their going. Dressed in her fur coat and a beautiful hat with a feather curving down to her shoulder, Doris stood shivering at her window which was open to us children and to the grey meagre snow of January in Lochfoot. That day, even Doris could not look gay.

'In the name o' the Kingdom o' Heaven,' she said, 'what a hell o' a place this is nooadays. I'll miss ye all, right enough but this place is no' for me. It'd send me aff my bliddy chump.'

And so, having given us all farewell pennies, Doris went away and my mother and Miss Miller said: 'Good riddance of bad rubbish,' and by the Easter holidays the Arms was full of smug old women and their fat husbands with gold watch-chains across their waistcoats, wealthy suburban people from Glasgow, in the main, down for 'a short holiday and a change in the country.' They did not have gramophones with pink horns and they did not sit at open windows. They sat round at the other side of the Arms in the glassed-in place that was called the veranda, looking at the view across the loch. Unlike Doris, they preferred the view to us children and this led us to develop a new pastime, while a new war cry rose out of the ground. We took to dancing along the stony shore of the loch under the glass veranda, making hideous faces at the people up above, mimicking the woman who was so fat that she could not walk but waddled, mimicking the fat man who stuck his thumbs in the armholes of his waistcoat, while we shouted: "Pollokshields! Pollokshields!

Pease brose and pianos!' in high shrill voices until Beery-belly came and chased us away.

The next to leave were the Belgies. They too told us that they were leaving, going back home to Belgium and Madame Fenchel cried and kissed us all. Grammar still had her white hair but she had no jewellery now except the brooch at her throat. The ear pendants had disappeared first and then the watch with its long chain and the true love knot made of pearls and although I do not remember anybody telling me so, I knew that these things had been sold to buy food and pay the rent of the Paddies after she had no more money left at the office in Glasgow.

With some of my war profits from beer bottles and guddled trout, I had acquired quite a stock of penny notebooks and pencils. I bought them from Tommy's where the Penny Library was. The notebooks, covered in red and blue glossy paper stood in a pile on a shelf and the pencils, red, blue and yellow, lay in a box beside them and I could easily have pinched both, but I always paid for them although I do not know why. Nor do I know why I bought them at all. I hardly ever wrote in them but there was one red one in which I noted, when I remembered, the titles of the books I had read. I had an indescribable satisfaction, however, in knowing that I had all these notebooks and pencils concealed in my hole in the wash-house wall and on a wet day I would go in there and con over my hoard, rubbing my finger-tips over the blue and red gloss of the covers, rolling the pencils between my hands, like a miser running gold through his fingers, like my mother, indeed, sighing over the pennies in her kist.

The day after Doris went away, it came over me that I had been very stupid. I should have asked her for the address of the place to which she was going, have written it in one of my notebooks and then, after I went to work and had money to pay a train fare, I could have gone to see her one day. I decided that I was not going to be so stupid about Madame Fenchel and Grammar. It was unlikely that I would ever have enough money to pay the fare all the way to Belgium but, as a matter of principle and to strike a blow against my own stupidity, I would ask for their addresses all the same so, on the Friday evening that was to be the Belgies' last evening at the Paddies, I put a new blue note-book and a new blue pencil up the leg of my knickers.

When I asked about the address, Madame was delighted. She made me understand that, first of all, they were all going to the home of her nephew and that this address would always find her and Grammar, but when she told me the address, I could not spell it, so she herself had to write it in my book. Her writing was as queer and foreign as the address and herself, but there it was in my book, something to be proud of: 'Madame Fenchel, Les Cloches, St. Augustine, Courtrai, Belgique.'

The next morning, when I went down with the others to the Paddies and found it deserted, I could not believe that the Belgies had really gone although, only the evening before, Madame had told me that they were to leave on the early morning train. There was nothing left of them now except the dustbin at the door and the address in my blue notebook. We stood around the fence for a little while, then somebody opened the gate and, in a concerted rush, we attacked the wooden door with stones and did not stop until it was all pitted and scarred, by which time Beery-belly had arrived to chase us away.

Once again, my mother and Miss Miller said: 'Good riddance of that foreign rubbish. Imagine eating eels! The vulgarity of it!' for, naturally, it had become known that the Belgies ate eels. They had been known to ask for them at the fish shop, in the early days, before I and one or two others saw to their supplies.

Doris had given us all pennies before she left but the

Belgies had no pennies to give us. All they left behind in Lochfoot was a memory, the address in my notebook and Marie-Bernadette's baby, up in the cemetery. There was a garden up Lochview that was one carpet of snowdrops under its bare winter trees. I pinched a cardboard box from the Co-op dustbin, went up Lochview all by myself in the dark of a February evening and tore up the snowdrops in handfuls until the big box was full. I then went to the cemetery in the hideous dark, climbed over the wall and made my way over the spongy grass of the graves and among the horrible slabs and pillars of standing stone to the grave with the little white cross at the top. Under the thin, cold February moon, the snowdrops covered the grave like a white blanket and the Milky Way tumbled across the sky like a sparkling ever-rolling stream.

CHAPTER EIGHT

Work, for the night is coming!
Work through the morning hours;
Work while the dew is sparkling;
Work 'mid springing flowers;
Work while the day grows brighter,
Under the glowing sun;
Work, for the night is coming,
When man's work is done.

HYMN 357

BY THE SUMMER OF 1919, my mother was a well-known and highly respected member of the Lochfoot community. Her image, which was a true one in its outer aspects, was that of the hard-working respectable widow woman who kept her child fed, clean and clothed and was unsparing in her efforts to keep her home together. During my father's lifetime, she had never gone beyond the backyard, except to the shops around the corner and in those years few people meeting her in the main street would have known her by name. She did not visit friends and she did not, like some women, go to the pub with her husband. She did not go to church either, because this would have meant the putting of a penny in the collection plate, but she observed the Sabbath rigidly at home, neither knitting nor sewing, but reading her *People's Friend* quietly by the side of the grate in which there was no fire.

After my father was killed and the mangle came, my mother changed. The mangle was the badge of a new freedom within which her personality could develop unrestrained, so that her desire for wealth began to flourish like some rank growth that was unconfined and unpruned. In a natural way, the collecting and delivering of mangled

156

laundry took her out into the streets and into the homes of the town, a neat douce figure in her dark grey costume that was pale at the elbows with age, her plain black hat and her black buttoned shoes. She had never gone as far as the Co-op round the corner without putting on her hat, anchoring it to her hair with long pins that had discs of jet the size of pennies at their ends. It was vulgar to go out without a hat, just as it was vulgar to go to the pub or 'raking about the streets, visiting and gossiping'. But, of course, it was not vulgar to rake about the streets, visit people and 'pass the time of day', which was her euphemistic description of what was otherwise gossiping, if you did these things 'in the way of your work'. Only the most vulgar and shiftless people did not accept that 'to work and get on' was the reason for and lynch-pin of human existence unless you had been born a 'rich toff' into one of the villas in Lochview Crescent.

And now my mother's attitude to Sunday changed also. God, it now became apparent, would not send a respectable hard-working widow woman to Hell if she tried to turn an honest penny by doing some mangling on Sundays but, as we have seen, Miss Miller put a stop to the Sunday mangling. However, my mother, who truly believed that God smiled upon hard workers who indulged in no vulgar extravagance and stored their money to improve their circumstances, confident that God was on her side, began to do our washing at the kitchen sink on Sunday forenoons, storing it in cold water to be hung out on Monday morning and our mending and other quiet tasks on Sunday afternoons, so that she would have the weekdays free to clank the mangle, unmolesting and unmolested by Miss Miller. Miss Miller continued to pass on the *People's Friend* but it was no longer read, except by myself in the privacy of the water closet.

But Sunday washing and mending and weekday mangling were not enough. The addiction to money has a feature in common with all other addictions, which is the appetite that grows by what it feeds on. The more alcohol taken in, the greater the need for more alcohol, the more books read, the greater the need to read more books, the more money stored in the kist, the greater the need for more money to store in the kist.

Thus, the mangle was only a temporary assuagement of my mother's discontent. By her willingness to deliver the finished work, she had attracted the patronage of most of old Mrs. Gurney's customers and was now filling Lochfoot's demand for mangling, but she still had time left over, time for more work. The smouldering volcano of her discontent began to erupt in fierce attacks on my granny and Miss Miller, when she walked to and fro across our kitchen, spitting venom.

I have already remarked that I came through my childhood unscathed by measles, chickenpox or impetigo, although almost constantly in contact with these contagions and have suggested that my immunity may have been related to my mental attitude. I have also said that the departure of my father and his work-mates to the war had about it the atmosphere of an 'up Lochview' and I would now go further and say that the Great War would never have taken place had there not been a human will, in the rank and file like my father, towards war. The circumstances and pressures that bent the will in that direction are another matter. What is cogent is that the will to war had been created.

And now, in the summer of 1919, as I listened to my mother storming, her will to work and to wealth battering at the barriers of life, I came to the conviction, although I could not have put it into words at that time, that this monstrous will of hers must bend events. Something, I was sure, was bound to happen and something did. As a single event, unrelated to other events, it had little importance, but no event, however unimportant, stands in isolation. Old Joe, who had managed old Pillans's Secondhand ever since I could remember, was found dead of drink in the back shop at last. My mother offered herself to fill his place and was accepted at once.

The immediate effect on myself was of being thrust into a black pit of horror and desolation from which it was not possible, even, to cry out in protest. In the house, I looked on dumbly at my mother's self-satisfaction in her new position while, out of doors, I tried to avoid my companions without, at the same time, letting the avoidance be obvious. Outwardly defiant, inwardly shamed almost beyond bearing, I ignored the cries of: 'How's old Pillans's shop woman?' and laid about me when my skirt was tweaked from behind and the taunt came: 'Poor stuff! No' worth but tuppence—Pillans's price—tuppence!' And when I ran away from their tweaking and taunting, they would call after me: 'Away an' work for Pillans! Away an' help your ma!'

The aspect of it all that I found most hurtful and unjust was that I was basically in agreement with the tweakers and taunters. I myself would have treated in this way anyone who was connected with old Pillans, but there was no way to explain to my fellows that the connection between my mother and myself was so slight and tenuous that it had not the strength to flow through her to connect myself to old Pillans. There was no means of explaining that I scorned and hated her job at the Secondhand, no way to make them understand that I was powerless against this circumstance. There are always compensations, however. Inside the walls of Number Three Railway Terrace, there was now peace and satisfaction and I did not have to worry about the welfare of my granny any more. My mother was in all-day attendance at the Secondhand only on Fridays and Saturdays and if she were required at other times, a card in the window told where she could be found. In this way, she still had ample time and energy to attend to the mangling and wore a prosperous satisfied air, remarking again and again that her post at the

Secondhand meant 'regular money coming in, not being chancy, like mangling'.

By the end of the summer holidays, the atmosphere out doors among the tribe improved also. Perhaps my own resistant will had had its effect or perhaps it was the operation of the law of life that nothing lasts for ever. The taunting and tweaking came to an end. My mother's place in the community had shifted but I had reverted to my former status as a unit of the mob that attacked the guests at the Arms, the villas of Lochview, the doorbells of the main street and went trespassing Up-the-Burn-to-the-Dam.

No sooner had life settled down again, however, than my mother made another new departure. I have an idea that, when she undertook the management of the Secondhand, she found herself subjected to pressures more subtle than the taunting and tweaking of my fellows. Certainly, the amount of laundry that came to our house to be mangled dropped off at once and when my mother made a delivery, it took her less time than formerly, for she was no longer invited across the thresholds of the houses that she visited. The image of the respectable hard-working widow woman began to fade and something more sinister to take its place, so that when she walked along the street, there was a tendency for the neighbours to pass her by with only a murmured greeting and a tendency for the children to stand staring silently from a distance for a moment until one of them would say, in a voice of higher pitch than the normal: 'Ach, it's only Mrs. Robertson the Railie.' On these occasions, to my relief, they did not say: 'Ach, it's only Jeanie's ma,' although this would have been the more usual phrase. This meant that, in the minds of my companions, the slight sinister aura did not extend to myself.

My mother suddenly decided that she and I would attend church on Sunday forenoons and it was obvious to me that the decision had importance in her mind, because she took some money out of the kist one night, made a trip to the town

Down-the-line the next day and returned with new clothes for herself and a coat, hat, buttoned boots, stockings and gloves for myself. Except for the heavy black laced boots that I wore in winter, these were the only clothes that were not second-hand that I could remember owning and, as I looked at them, a line from a hymn echoed in my mind. For once in my life, I was to be 'in new bright raiment clad' because my mother was going to declare her respectability to the community at large, to demonstrate that this respectability could remain unsullied in spite of her turning an honest penny at old Pillans's Secondhand. She was very fond of the phrase 'to turn an honest penny'.

For me, when the novelty of the new clothes wore off, the church-going became a mixture of small pleasure and large restricting nuisance. The pleasure lay in the amusement to be had from observing how different people were in church but this was far outweighed by the fact that there was no Up-the-Burn on Sunday forenoons. Hitherto, this had been an excellent time for Up-the-Burn, for old Stink was a regular church-goer and it was said that these two hours on Sundays were the only times when he laid aside his stick. Also, church meant that I came home after the long dreary sermon, had my dinner and then went straight back to Sunday school in the church hall.

The church itself I found interesting. It was only when I went inside it for the first time, through the porch between the fishmonger's and the fish and chip shop, that I discovered that it was not part of the Lochfoot town that I knew. It was much older, as old as the Village and old Pillans's place and as I sat, facing the pulpit, it was as if I could see through the wall behind it into the garden of the manse, across the garden to the manse itself and beyond the manse to the cemetery higher up the hill. The church, garden, manse and cemetery were an old island, around which modern Lochfoot had been built, fishmonger's and fish and chip shop joined ruthlessly to the old walls of the porch, rendering invisible the lines of the old building.

After my first visit to church, I paid a visit to my granny and asked her about it.

'Aye,' she told me, 'the kirk, the manse and the kirkyard were there since ever I mind.'

'And what was where the fishmonger's and the other shops are now?'

'What d'ye think? There was a bit o' grass and some trees round the kirk and the manse and the burial ground and then a bit wall and then the parks o' Castleside.'

'Castleside?'

'Aye. Castleside Farm. It was after they built the shops on to the kirk that your gran'father and I stopped attendin'. If the kirk itsel' is that keen on money that it has to sell the kirk green for a fish shop, your gran'father said, I'll read my Bible in my own place, away from the smell o' fish guts an' that's what we did. So your mother's taking ye to the kirk, Jean?'

'Aye.'

'Well, well. Fill the kettle for some tea, lass.'

My granny, although I was sure that she knew about it, never mentioned my mother's working at the Secondhand. Her only comment took the form, frequent with her, of no comment. Formerly, when I visited her, she used to say at some point: 'And your mother is keeping well, Jean?' and I would reply: 'Aye, Granny. She's fine,' but after my mother went to the Secondhand, this formal little enquiry was dropped. My mother was no longer mentioned at Lilac Cottage.

The management of the Secondhand meant that fewer pennies than silver coins and even notes went into the kist on Saturday nights but, while the kist grew fatter and fatter, our way of life seemed to become thinner and thinner. The purchase of the new clothes for church-going was the only expenditure that my mother undertook and even this she tried to recoup by further household economies.

By 1920, the pattern of the aftermath of war began to take shape. There came a quiet change in the aspect of Lochfoot and a veil of drab dreariness descended over the township. The suburban people continued to come to the Arms for weekends and short holidays but they belonged to a race apart from the Railies and Trammies who constituted the mass of the population. And many of these people now came down to Lochfoot in their own cars, instead of using the railway while the business men of Lochview Crescent also began to travel up and down to their Glasgow offices by car and were no longer to be seen, in their black suits, converging on the railway station in the mornings. The trains and tramcars on which the Lochfoot outside of the old Village and Lochview Crescent depended were used less and less. The war had opened up new areas on the outskirts of Glasgow as training camps, storage dumps and hospitals and now that the war was over, these new areas began to develop into industrial suburbs. The tide of prosperity, which had been at its height at about the turn of the century, began to ebb away from Lochfoot.

The Railway Company and the Tramways Corporation began to pay off men, for both were moving their maintenance depots to more centralized sites, so that the people began to drift away too, in the wake of the machines of the second Iron Age. Railway Terrace and Tramway Buildings became more and more dilapidated, being the property of the Company and the Corporation. They had the look of places about which nobody cared. Nobody had ever cared about them very much but there had been a time when railway and tramway had depended upon the men who lived in them, so that a roof that leaked had been repaired. But nowadays, if the water closet blocked up, there was no plumber to be called from the Railway Works and old Lewie Leadpipe, the town plumber, had to be paid for his services.

At this time too, the authorities embarked on a policy of housing the Tinkers who, from time immemorial, had been a nomadic drifting population, living in caravans, tents, under the overhang of a disused quarry and the like. The younger members of this separate race were ready and willing to come under the shelter of a roof, having been forced to be accustomed to the indoors in school, but the older members presented a problem, for they suffered, no doubt, from claustrophobia of which the authorities showed little understanding.

To my mother's and Miss Miller's loud-voiced disgust, several Tinker families were moved into Railway Terrace and I was told that if I as much as spoke to any of them, I would suffer for it, although for all of my school days I had sat side by side in class with any Tinker children who could be rounded up from the encampment at the Old Dam and 'whipped in' to school by the 'Whipper-in'' or School Board Officer. These Tinker children who had joined the main child tribe only occasionally in the past, for a special trip up Lochview or the like now became permanent members of the roving gang and they brought to it a new life, a new ingenuity, a knowledge much more detailed of the ways of nature than any of us Railies and Trammies had ever had. In the forbidden world of Up-the-Burn, they were in their element and old Stink and his minions suffered depredations to the property they guarded such as they had never experienced before. The Tinker boys had ferrets, they had mongrel dogs that could move as secretly and to purpose as deadly as snakes in the grass and the boys knew precisely how to set snares that would be invisible even to old Stink and yet in places where rabbits were sure to be caught in them.

The favourite Tinker with all of us children was, of course, old Sandy to whose bagpipes we had danced throughout the war and we were delighted when it became known that blind authority had directed that Sandy and all his numerous descendants were to be housed in the end house of Railway Terrace, the corner one with three apartments that corresponded with Miss Miller's house at our end and in the two-roomed house above. Sandy and his descendants were surnamed Cameron and we were even more delighted when authority decreed that the hereditary enemies of the Cameron Tinkers, surnamed MacPhee, were to be put into the other two houses, served by the same close. My mother and Miss Miller were horrified, even old Beery-belly, that lickspittle to authority, protested to the powers for once that Camerons and MacPhees crammed together like this must lead to an explosion. Authority, however, deaf as well as blind, had made the decree and upheld it, while we of the child tribe looked forward with glee to the evening when one Cameron or one MacPhee had enough money to buy that one drink too many which would act as a detonator.

The MacPhees, some twenty-five to thirty of them, settled peaceably enough into their four rooms, as did the younger Camerons into their five, but Sandy and his wife Mary would have no truck with the narrow close entrance and the floor of a room under them, while four walls rose round them and a ceiling pressed down on them from above. Nor would they be parted from Kitchener, the old horse who had drawn their little two-wheeled float the length and breadth of Scotland nor from their mongrel dog Hector, who was named not after the hero of Troy but after the Highland general, Hector Macdonald. There was a wash-house allotted to each four houses in the Terrace. These were low brick buildings, built in lean-to form in a row against the wall at the bottom of the backyard and each contained a cold water tap, a black boiler which would be fired from underneath and two round wooden wash-tubs which sat upon a brick-built pedestal. Sandy found the wash-house that belonged to the houses that the Camerons and MacPhees had been given an ideal stable for Kitchener and kennel for Hector. Kitchener's bed of straw occupied most of the small stone floor, while his hay occupied one of the wash-tubs and his drinking water the other but Kitchener did not like to be entirely confined within walls any more than did his master and, one day, he turned his hind-quarters to the small square window and kicked out glass, frame and all. After that, Kitchener could look out upon the world at any time he chose and see what was going on.

Kitchener occupying most of the floor with his bed and his heap of dung, Hector slept in the bottom of the zinc boiler on a heap of old rags and he got himself into this high bed by taking a leap from the doorway on to Kitchener's recumbent side and another leap from there into the boiler, for Hector was a very agile dog who, as I have told, could walk about on his hind legs with a tin mug hung on a string round his neck, begging for pennies when his master played the bagpipes.

We children had one thing in common with Sandy and the adult Tinkers which we did not share with any other group of adults and this was the war against authority. The authorities did not approve of Kitchener and Hector living in the wash-house while Sandy and Mary slept, as they had always done, under their little cart, draped with a tarpaulin to make a tent, outside in the yard by the wash-house door. The authorities disapproved of quite a number of things that the Tinkers did and did not do, such as tipping their sewage out of buckets over the wall into the Burn, instead of sending it respectably to the Burn through the medium of the water closets. And they disapproved of the Tinkers using the water closet bowls to wash their potatoes in, while the festoons of rabbit skins, drying out on the iron railings of the upstairs balcony, being such a public offence, they approved of still less.

When authority, in the form of the 'Poorie', which was our rendering of 'Poor Inspector', came round to protest about these matters, there were doings of great moment. Every Railie, Trammie and Tinker child rallied to the aid of Sandy, Kitchener and Hector with pocketfuls of stones, paper bags and other receptacles from the shop dustbins filled with water, rotten eggs and fish-heads and guts from the yard of the fish shop, with which ammunition we set up such a barrage that

166

the Poorie, accompanied by Beery-belly and Macaroni came only twice and never came back. Kitchener continued to live in his wash-house and look out of his window, twitching his ears at the world.

Hector and Kitchener were probably the best-fed creatures in Railway Terrace too, for the tribe found a new amusement in stealing carrots from the Co-op for Kitchener and sausages from the butcher for Hector. These pinchings were usually carried out by Jenny Smith and myself, two thin, fragile-looking bare-footed waifs with wispy fair curls, who would arrive on the pavement outside the chosen shop with our chalk and draw on the pavement the 'beds' for a game of 'Peever', which in some places is called Hopscotch and in other places Kettlack. One hopped, pushing an empty boot-blacking tin from bed to bed with the hopping foot.

While Jenny and I hopped and the tin slid clinking along the pavement, there would be a sudden diversion in the back-yard of the shop, drawing off the staff and in a trice Jenny and I were inside and the sausages or carrots were up the legs of our elastic-bound knickers. When the people in the shop came back, having chased away these rough boys from their dust-bins in the backyard, the two innocent waifs would still be hopping along, completely immersed in their skills with their blacking-tin peever. Then, back at Railway Terrace, there was the pleasure shared by all of giving Kitchener or Hector a really tasty meal.

Miss Miller and my mother continued to draw down their upper lips in disapproval of the roystering life at the other end of the Terrace and for a time my mother tried to keep me away from the Tinkers but I was persistent in my atten-dance on Sandy, Kitchener and Hector so that, in time, she discontinued her efforts, for she needed all her energy for more profitable pursuits.

Railway Terrace continued to disintegrate round us. The water closet did not work at all now, because neither Miss

Miller nor my mother would pay old Lewie Leadpipe to repair it. Miss Miller's old brother was now retired from the railway and living on his small pension. My mother took the view that a poor widow woman should not be asked to repair the closet and Miss Miller took the view that a working woman with a regular pay coming in was in a better position to pay for such repairs than a poor old pensioner so they both resorted to tipping pails over the wall into the Burn like the Tinkers that they so despised. Miss Miller and my mother looked upon themselves as virtuous martyrs, as they carried out this darksome duty at dead of night, because it had been thrust upon them by circumstances and was not a matter of choice as in the case of the Tinkers. In such unlikely ways can the boundary between virtue and vice be delineated.

While my mother put money into the kist coin by coin and note by note, she became more and more withdrawn into herself. Since she began to work at the Secondhand, Miss Miller spoke to her less and less and, nowadays, it required a major scandal, like the housing of the Tinkers, to bring them together in disapproval and indignation.

In the spring of 1920, I reached the stage of gradual graduation out of the child gang and was looking forward to leaving school at the end of June when the summer holidays would begin. To leave school meant to begin to work, but I considered myself fortunate in that there was no need for me to do domestic service up Lochview because, since the Belgies had left, something new had developed down at the Paddies. The old building now had a big white board above its door that said: 'O.K. Shirts Ltd.' It had been gutted out, had had its windows de-netted and enlarged and was now a factory where shirts were made. It employed only one man, who was the manager and the rest of its workers were women and girls, mostly girls who went there as soon as they left school. Maisie Anderson, in whose care I first went to school, had been working there since it first opened and she said it was far better than service up Lochview, cheery, among a crowd like yourself all the time and plenty of fun at piece-time in the middle of the day, instead of creeping about in a cap and apron up at The Beeches, as if you had no right to open your mouth just because you were a servant. The shirt factory would suit me very well, I thought, giving more pay than service up Lochview and, in addition, Sundays free to go Up-the-Burn, a pastime to which I was still addicted.

For once, without discussion much less argument, my mother and I were in agreement. She approved of my plan that I should apply for work at the shirt factory when the time came and I knew very clearly why she approved. If I went into domestic service, I would be 'living in' and might refuse to hand over to her any of my pay, as I had refused to hand over the mangling-delivery pennies, but working at the shirt factory, I would be living at home and would have to contribute the value of my bed and board to the household economy.

The first cloud shadow fell upon my plans in the Easter holidays of 1920, one day when I was visiting my granny and told her what I intended to do.

'You are going to work in that place?' she asked quietly and then added: 'I thought you would rather go into good service.'

'*I'm* not going to be a slavey up Lochview!' I said scornfully.

'Lochview!' my granny said and her quiet scorn was much more scorching than my own loud words had been. 'I was speaking of *good* service. There will be an opening for a fifth housemaid at the Castle by the summer. Teenie Gilmour that's the second is getting married and the rest will be moving up.'

I had a fleeting memory of the back courtyard of the Castle, as I had seen it from my form in the undergrowth, the giggling maids in their trim blue and white, the jokes with the gardeners and the vanmen who called, but it was only an otherworldly vision, as was everything pertaining to the Castle in my mind. The reality was the shirt factory or Lochview and I was set upon the shirt factory. For the first time in my life, my granny tried to influence me.

'I can understand your mother wanting you to go to that place, Jean,' she said, coming more into the open about my mother than she had ever done before, 'but money isn't everything. If you are properly trained in a good house, where you will see things done as they should be, it will stand by you all your life. You are not tall enough for table work—they like tall handsome girls for the front o' the house and you are just wee and bonnie. And you are not strong enough for the kitchen, although I grant you you are wiry and healthy. But upstairs work would suit you down to the ground, quick and tidy as you can be. And you would be well fed and in good company all the time. Things are very cheery in the hall at the Castle.'

'The hall?'

'The servants' hall,' she explained. 'You think about it, Jean. Think twice between now and the summer.'

That word 'servants' turned the fortune of the day. I did not think about my future any more. I was determined to apply at the shirt factory with every certainty of being employed for the big door was open to swallow willingly every girl who left school. I was not to know, at that time, that when girls grew a little older, when they had worked for four years, perhaps and wanted a little more pay, the manager paid them off and saw them out from the little new back door from his office at the far end. After all, in 1920, Maisie Anderson had been at the factory for only a little over a year and she was one of its first employees.

When I was alone in some quiet place and the thought of going to work in the shirt factory came to the forefront of my mind, it seemed queer, frightening and incomprehensible. Fourteen years ago, I had been born, because my mother and father, like all married people, had done That in bed one night. They had not done it in order that I might be born.

Nobody in their senses went out of their way to burden themselves with another mouth to feed. They had done it because it was a thing that married people did and I was the unfortunate result. It was humiliating to feel that you were no more than an unfortunate result and it would be better if you could go on believing in the childish tale that God had sent you in the doctor's black bag as a present to your mother. If this tale had been true, God, who knew everything that people said and did and even thought, would have had more sense than to send me to my mother, for he would have known that a baby was not the sort of present she would like. At this, I had a thought that made me smile inside my head. God would have sent my mother a mangle or an Iron Man instead.

Silly tales about doctors' black bags aside, here I was, fourteen years old and in a few weeks I would go to work in the shirt factory. Why had I been born? To grow to fourteen years old and go to work in the shirt factory? By all I had seen and been taught, it seemed so, although when I thought of the world of Up-the-Burn, where the primroses were in bloom just now, it seemed very strange. Yet, that was how it was. All the other children I had known had grown to be fourteen years old and go to work, all except Isabel Adair and her brothers, that was, for Colin was already at the Academy Down-the-line and soon Isabel would be going to Glasgow University. But Isabel and her brothers were Villagers and Villagers were different. Suddenly I remembered that my father had said once that Adairs had been shepherds to the Castle for generations. None of this latest lot of Adair boys were going to be shepherds. You could not learn to be a shepherd at the university. Life was changing for the Adairs, but then it was changing for me too. I was not going to be a domestic servant like all the Railie girls who had gone before me, I was going to work in a shirt factory.

One thing was certain, I told myself Sunday after Sunday, as I sat beside my prim-faced kid-gloved mother, while old

Poopit from high above lectured his congregation about sin and sloth. When I had left school and was working at the shirt factory, I would be finished with church for good. When I had my own pay-packet every Saturday, I would be able to do as I pleased and this dim place, where no light could get in except at front and back because it was hemmed in on both sides by the brick of fish and fish and chips shops, would see me no more. My mother could attend church by herself.

Sitting beside me, putting her penny into the collection plate, she had a satisfied look as if she had just made a lucrative investment in respectability. She had the air that she wore when she had added a few more coins to the kist or when she had just bought in a particularly good bargain for the Secondhand. My mother's love of financial gain had a crystalline purity. It was intrinsic, so that she loved a gain made for old Pillans as much—or nearly so—as she loved a gain made for herself.

The collection taken up, Miss Miller at the organ and Lewie Leadpipe the plumber, standing alongside at the bellows, prepared to play the final hymn and before old Poopit announced it, I knew that it would be Number 357, for both Miss Miller and old Lewie were metaphorically rolling up their sleeves. When the hymn was announced, they began to play a verse of the tune and on the first note, as if to emphasize its importance, Lewie pressed down hard with both both hands on the handle of the bellows while Miss Miller's coat was strained across her back with effort. We all stood and began to sing:

> '*Work*, for the night is coming!
> *Work*, through the morning hours;
> *Work*, while the dew is sparkling;
> *Work*, 'mid springing flowers—'

The only place where I had ever seen dew sparkling or flowers springing, unplanted and of their own accord, was

Up-the-Burn and I could not imagine working among them. Work of the kind that this hymn demanded meant clanking a mangle or cinders flying as at the railway siding or buying and selling dirty old carpets at the Secondhand. If you did these things Up-the-Burn, the dew would cease to sparkle and the flowers to spring, so that the magic land would be destroyed and become only a memory, like my granny's memory of the one-time green field.

CHAPTER NINE

Change and decay in all around I see;
O Thou who changest not, abide with me.

ONE SATURDAY EVENING early in June, my mother came home from the Secondhand looking more than usually pleased with herself. She had even been to the butcher's to buy two sausages for tea and as she put the frying-pan on the gas-ring, she said: 'I spoke to Mr. Pillans about ye the-day. He says you can start as soon as the school comes out.'

'Start what?' I asked.

'At the shirt factory, of course.'

'The shirt factory? What has that got to do with old Pillans?'

'None of your cheek,' she told me, 'and less of your vulgarity as well. The gentleman's name is *Mister* Pillans.'

Until she went to work at the Secondhand, my mother had always referred to Pillans as 'old Pillans' as did the rest of Lochfoot but I was more interested in his apparent impingement on my personal life than in my mother's new attitude to him. I was more than interested. I was furiously angry when I thought that he might even have spoken my name. It was as if I had been touched by a hideous slimy tentacle.

'He's old Pillans to *me*,' I said angrily, 'just as he's always been. What the hell is it to do with old Pillans whether I go to the shirt factory or not? You had no bloody business to——'

'Don't you swear at *me*, Jeanie Robertson! The vulgarity of it—swearing at your own mother!'

'Don't call me Jeanie. My name is Jean.' I thumped the table with my fist. 'Why did you go blethering about *me* to that humpy-backed slimy old b——'

174

'You stop that this minute or you'll suffer for it. Mr. Pillans *owns* the shirt factory, you stupid brat!'

All the anger ran out through the soles of my feet. My fists opened, my fingers became limp and with weak knees I sank down on my wooden chair beside the table while I watched the dark snake-like tentacle reach out under the ground from the Secondhand and grope its way under streets and buildings before coming to the surface and curling itself in a tight grip round the shirt factory in the old Paddies.

My mother, turning the sausages with a fork, was looking more secretly pleased with herself than ever.

'It's not commonly known that he owns it,' she said in a satisfied way. 'Mr. Pillans knows what's what and keeps his business to himself.' Brooding over the cleverness of Pillans, proud that she knew more of his affairs than the rest of Lochfoot, she was unaware of the effect of her information on myself and, as she looked down into the frying pan, she was talking more to herself than to me. 'He fairly knows how many beans make five, better than anybody in Lochfoot, better than them up at Lochview, even, that think themselves so clever. None o' *them* saw, when the war came, that there would be Belgies needing a place to live or that officers from abroad on leave had had to have a place to go. D'ye know all he paid to the Railway Company for the Paddies? Ten pound. Just ten pound! If that's not good business, let somebody tell me what is.'

Over the sausages and fried potatoes, she gloated over the cleverness of old Pillans while my mind tried to encompass the fantastic information she was spilling. 'I don't know how much he paid for the Arms, but it wouldna be much, the state it was in. I've never seen any o' the papers for the Arms, just the shirt factory. I check the accounts for the factory. But the Arms pays all right, even now, you can bet your boots, apart from making a fortune during the war. Mr. Pillans is not the man to keep on something that doesn't make a profit.'

My mind became more and more muddled. During the war, the Belgies had been vulgar, foreign and disgusting with their eel-eating and other filthy habits and whoever had given them permission to move into that dirty old Paddies place ought to have been shot, for it was not fit even for Belgies to live in. During the war, the Arms had been a disgrace and the people who frequented it shameless and sunk below all decency but now, in the light reflected from old Pillans's hoarded profits, all this was changed, just as old Pillans was changed into Mister Pillans, the clever gentleman who knew what was what and how many beans made five.

Having finished my meal, I rose from the table while my mother was still thinking aloud and with admiration of her employer's acumen and as I opened the door to the close, she became conscious of my presence.

'Here, you,' she said, 'don't you go blethering outside about anything I've said. Mind that. The main thing about business matters is that they're private.' I had a certainty that the last sentence was a quotation from that master of the what's what, Pillans. 'Mr. Pillans's affairs are nobody's business and you keep your mouth shut.'

'I don't care a damn about his affairs,' I told her, 'and you can tell him from me what he can do with his bloody shirt factory.'

'Jeanie Robertson!'

'I wouldn't work for old Pillans if his damned factory was the last place on earth. I am going into good service,' I shouted and went out, pulling the door shut with a bang behind me.

I set out for my granny's house, staring hard and sternly at the ground to indicate to my friends gathered at the gable of the Terrace that, this evening, I was a 'big girl' with grave adult matters on her mind, who could not be bothered with childish things. When I rounded the corner to go down past the shops, Kingdom Come the Trammie was already in position at the kerb opposite the pub door, lustily singing his favourite hymn:

> *Abide with me; fast falls the eventide;*
> *The darkness deepens; Lord, with me abide;*
> *When other helpers fail, and comforts flee,*
> *Help of the helpless, O abide with me.*

My granny was in her little front garden, looking at her purple and gold 'Dusty Millers' as she called them but she seemed to understand that something untoward had happened and led me into the house.

'Granny,' I said when she was in her chair by the fire, 'I have changed my mind about working at the shirt factory. I would rather go up to the Castle, if I could.'

'I am glad you have changed your mind about that place, Jean,' she said quietly but then she gave a sharp little sigh, 'only I canna help ye about the Castle. They're not taking on another housemaid.'

'Not?'

'No.' She sighed again and looked into her fire for a time before she said: 'I might as well tell ye the whole thing, but not a word outside this house, Jean, even to your mother. They'll all know soon enough. His Grace himself came down to see me yesterday.'

'His Grace?' For a moment, I thought that my granny had gone soft in the head as some old people did and was imagining that God had paid her a visit.

'The Duke, lassie,' she said a little impatiently, 'the Duke from the Castle. Jean, he is selling out the estate.'

As far as penetrating to my understanding went, she might have been addressing me in Greek, for she was speaking of a way of life and matters pertaining to it that were utterly foreign to me. Very slowly, I began to understand that my granny lived in Lilac Cottage because she was a pensioner, as my grandfather had been before he died, of the Duke, that all the houses in the Village were occupied by pensioners and employees of the Duke. Still more slowly did I come to understand that three young men, to whom my granny referred as 'the three young masters' and to whom she had once been schoolroom maid, had been killed at the war. While she spoke, my mind kept flying off at tangents as it tried to translate into Railway Terrace terms what she was saying and it was momentarily filled with a picture of Tellypete, swerving showily from side to side on his red bicycle, as he rode up one of those long beech-vaulted drives to the Castle with a telegram in his leather pouch. The most difficult thing for me to understand was that the vast territory enclosed by the twelve-foot stone wall was a commodity that could be sold, sold like a sausage over the butcher's counter or an old table at Pillans's Secondhand. To try to comprehend this was literally to feel the earth move under my feet.

'It is a funny thing,' my granny was saying, 'when I think now o' my father telling when the Castle was being built.'

'Being built?' I repeated, realizing for the first time, I think, that that huge bulk of stone, those pepperpot turrets, those battlements biting into the sky like square blunt teeth were the work of human hands.

'Aye. It's not that old, ye know, the Castle. Maybe fifteen year older than me but that's about all. The *old* castle that they pulled down before they built this one was different. It was as old as the hills, they tell me.'

'And they pulled it down?'

I was floundering about in the strange waters of time that my granny was conjuring up from the fountain of her memory as if I had been swept over the rim of the Dam and caught in the glass curtain of water that poured over and down into the Burn.

'Och, aye. It was when the old Duchess—His Grace's mother that's dead and gone this twenty year and more—came to the Castle as a bride. She had plenty money o' her own, forbye what the Duke had and she was needing a new castle like the one the old Queen put up for herself at Balmoral. So they pulled down the old one and put up the new one. But what was it I was saying, Jean?'

'About your father telling about when the new one was getting built.'

'Aye, aye. There was workmen came from all over for the building of it, from London, some o' them and some from Italy, even, to put down the tiles in the floor o' the main hall. One o' the Londoners, a joiner he was, as I mind, was a bit like Kingdom Come the Trammie up there in the town, for ever makin' speeches an' prophesyin' an' the like, but not religious like Kingdom Come. This man was for ever prophesyin' that the day would come when men like the old Duke would perish from the earth an' men like himself, the joiner, would be the lords o' creation. My father an' the other men *called* him the Lord o' Creation for a nick-name and said he was wrong in the head.' My granny was silent for one of her thoughtful little moments before she added: 'Well, it's them that lives the longest that sees the most and it seems to me that the Lord o' Creation wasn't that wrong in his head after all.'

'But who will *buy* the Castle?' I asked. 'Who in the world would have enough money to buy it and the woods and the Dam and——' I stopped short. I was displaying to my granny an illicit knowledge of the appurtenances of the Castle, but she did not notice.

'There's plenty o' money in the world,' she said. 'There'll be a buyer for the Castle all right but it'll not be folk like the Family, I doubt.' The capital letter was audible in her voice as she spoke the word 'family', the importance of the word in her mind transferred to her tongue. 'The Castle will go to some sharp businessman that made a fortune out o' the war, likely. That's what His Grace thinks. That's why he came to see us all down here yesterday, so that we can buy out our houses at his own price and not the new man's.'

179

'Your houses?' I looked round at the sturdy walls of the room. Where was the money to come from to buy this building? Was there enough in my mother's kist? If I stole it to buy my granny's house, would they let her go on living here after I went to prison?

'But I'll manage fine,' she was saying contentedly. 'Don't you worry about me, Your Grace, I told him. I can manage the four hundred and still have a bit left. Hugh the Forester —that was your gran'father, Jean—was always a careful man, Your Grace, I said, but not a mean man. Money is a good servant but a bad master, he used to say.' She paused, nodding her head for a little before she went on: 'Aye, I'll be all right, Jean, but what about you? If you don't go to the shirt place and I'm pleased you are not doing that, there's nothing here for you except Lochview as they call it. You're on the young side to go too far from home.'

'I'll be all right, Granny,' I assured her. In a world where castles changed hands, a wee smout like myself did not seem to be very important. 'Where will the Duke go?'

'Himself and the Duchess are planning to live on the shooting estate in Perthshire. It's a wee place bye's the Castle and only a staff o' five in the house but as His Grace says, they'll get used to their poorer circumstances in time.'

It was now that I discovered that the word 'poor' is relative and comparative in meaning. Hitherto, when people were said to be in poor circumstances, I had known that they were caught in a process that would lead in the end to a throwing-out, like the one that Doris had stopped in the alley round from the Arms. But the Duke and Duchess were not to suffer a throwing-out and just as well, I thought wryly for, now that my mother had taken old Joe's place, I might have been further disgraced by her wheeling the flat barrow up the drive to the Castle.

My mother tried hard to persuade me to revert to the shirt factory but I was more determined than I had ever been about anything that I was going to stay beyond the reach of the sinister coils of old Pillans. My mother, it seemed to me, had grown even harder and more mercenary since she began to work for him. Before she went to the Secondhand, she had scrimped and saved and slaved at her mangle to make money but now she schemed, staring at the wall with narrowed eyes, as if she were dreaming of another war when *she* would buy up an old building to rent to Belgies and an old hotel to turn into a brothel.

'If I hadn't married your father and got myself tied to this house when I was young,' she said more than once, 'I would be a rich woman by now.'

This was her new dream but I knew with certainty that it was only a dream. She often said too that my granny was an old fool but I knew that my granny was wiser than she. Even if my mother had not married my father and had not had Number Three Railway Terrace and me to look after when she was young, I knew that she would never have been a rich woman. Even if she had had the ten pounds to buy the Paddies—she probably *had* ten pounds saved when the war came, now that I thought of it—she would never have had the idea of buying the Paddies and renting it to the Belgies. She would never have thought of doing anything with ten pounds except locking it in her kist. She would not even risk putting money in the bank because banks could fail. My mother I came to see now did not have thoughts. All she had in her mind were copies of things that other people thought, like admiring the Iron Man and thinking him unvulgar because the Simpsons of Laurelbank had bronzes and thought them unvulgar. And now, since she had got to know old Pillans, her thoughts seemed to be more and more like copies of his thoughts. For myself, I was determined to keep well away from him, that there might be no danger of that sinister magic that surrounded him casting its shadow over me.

It was as easy to get a domestic post at Lochview as it was

to get into the shirt factory. Every holidays, Easter, summer and Christmas, there appeared in the window of Tommy's shop, stuck to the glass in front of the fly-blown china ornaments and the post cards of fat women in red and yellow striped bathing costumes, a rash of notices that read: 'Wanted: Girl as scullery-maid. Must be clean in work and person. Apply to So-and-so, Lochview Crescent.' So, on a Saturday forenoon, I took myself round to Tommy's window. There were a lot of cards and pieces of paper stuck to the window today and I had read nearly them all before I came to a sheet of paper headed: 'Laurelbank, Lochview Crescent, Lochfoot by Glasgow' which read: 'Wanted: Young girl suitable to train under Cook-housekeeper as house-tablemaid where three kept. Must be clean in work and person. Established Church. No Catholics. Apply Miss Simpson 2-3 afternoons.'

Down the years, since I had first begun to read these notices, before the shirt factory opened and I knew that life led straight from school to domestic service, I had hoped that when I was fourteen, Laurelbank would have a notice in the window so that I could go there and read all the books in the glass-doored case in the drawing-room. I had never had much anxiety about this because Laurelbank had a notice in nearly every holidays but it was comforting that an idea that had been with me for so long had turned into fact in the end.

After dinner, when my mother had gone to the Secondhand, I dressed myself as if for church, gloves and all and set off for Laurelbank while my companions of the backyards jeered me on the first part of my way with loud cries of 'Ow, Gussie, call yerself a swank?' and 'Mind yer feet afore they trip ye', as it was traditional to shout at anybody who was 'dressed' on any day except Sunday. As I went round the corner of Tramway Buildings, Maggie Graham stopped me, looked me over and said: 'Goin' for a job? Who to?'

'Laurelbank.'

'Ye're daft. I'm for the shirt factory. Besides, ye'll miss the scramble.'

I had forgotten about the scramble but when Maggie spoke of it I had a thrill of secret pleasure that I had a legitimate excuse for missing it. I have never liked scrambles. They were a thing that took place at weddings, the big weddings that were held in the church, not Railie or Trammie weddings that were held in the Terrace or the Buildings. These last were quite different. At Railie or Trammie weddings, old Poopit or the Roman Catholic priest came to the house, conducted the service and went away, whereupon everybody got drunk and there was usually a fairly entertaining fight as a finale which led to a lot of knocking up, down or through, but weddings in the church were holy sort of affairs, with the organ playing and the bride all dressed up in white and carrying a bunch of flowers. And, there being no show without Punch, Beery-belly was on the pavement outside the church door to keep us children in some sort of order while we waited for the scramble. At the end of the wedding, the organ began to play a different sort of tune, as if it were trying to sound happy instead of holy but, the organ being in charge of Miss Miller and Lewie Leadpipe, the holiness always won and the noise was like an elephant trying to dance. However, this was the signal for us to crowd round the door.

When the married pair were framed in the doorway of the church, the best man came out and threw a handful of halfpennies along the pavement and we children scrambled for them. I had never liked this. I had never liked scrambling in the gutter among the dirty water and herring scales, pushing and jostling and screaming and never once did I get a single halfpenny in a scramble although, being small, I was often knocked down by the bigger boys and girls in the rush. I was always trying to find excuses to avoid going to scrambles and it was very pleasant to have a legitimate one today.

'I know I'll miss it,' I told Maggie now with an air of

sullen regret, 'but my Ma worked at Laurelbank and she wants me to work there too and that old bitch Simpson is only seeing folk between two and three.'

This tale about my mother was a lie, of course. My mother did not even know that I was on my way to Laurelbank.

'Shame!' said Maggie with deep sympathy before she ran off to join the rest of the tribe and I went happily on my way.

When I went through the gateway between the pillars with 'Laurelbank' written on them, there seemed to be a lot of gravel drive between me and the house and there seemed to be still more between me and the back door which was right round at the other side and even then I had to go down a flight of stone steps between iron railings to get to it. The house was different round at this side, with no lace curtains at the windows but with iron bars protecting the glass on the outside. The door was opened by a fattish woman in a stale-looking black dress and a long white apron, with a bib and frills that went over her shoulders but it was less white and less fresh than a white apron should be.

'Well?' she said.

'I've come to see Miss Simpson about the job.'

She looked me down, then up and then she sniffed. 'Wait there,' she said, shut the door and went away but it was not long before she came back and said: 'All right. Come in.'

I followed her through a longish flagged passage past several doors, then up some stairs and through a swinging door which was covered all over with dark green cloth. We were now in a darkish hall and here I almost turned and ran away back down to the basement for, standing at the foot of the staircase, was an Iron Man which was the size of a real man, holding an iron pole with a big axe blade at its top. Across the hall from him there was a door, the upper half of which was made of coloured glass like the window behind the pulpit in church and this cast upon the iron figure glimmers of dark red, blue and amber which made me think of the fire of Hell. However, having come all this way, I squeezed down my panic, told myself that the thing was only a suit of armour something like that worn by Robert the Bruce in the picture in the history book and allowed the woman to push me in through a door she had opened, a door which she now shut again, leaving me on the inside.

The room contained more furniture than I had ever seen in my life, heavy dark furniture and a great deal of draperies of different kinds and sitting on either side of a large fire were two thin oldish women, dressed all in black. There was a stale smell of people sitting over a fire behind shut windows for a long time.

'What is your name?' the older-looking one asked.

'Jean Robertson.'

'Where do you live?'

'Number Three Railway Terrace.'

I remembered the day that I first went to school, as she now held out her hand and said: 'References?' As I had been about my address on that first day at school, I was at a loss now. What were references?

She looked annoyed. 'You have no letter about your character from the schoolmaster or the minister or *any*body?' she asked.

I felt a wavering of indecision. This could be a valid and honourable excuse for running away from this house that held the big Iron Man if, to obtain a job here, a letter was required from old Cock or old Poopit. But there were her final words 'or *any*body' which seemed to imply that I myself, applying for this job, was not anybody but a—a thing which had to be vouched for by someone like old Cock or old Poopit before these sour-faced old women would accept me as a person at all.

Suddenly, I was no longer involved in an effort to obtain a situation but in an attempt to assert my own identity, to assert it in the only way I knew, which was by outwitting the authority that treated me as a disposable chattel.

'My mother used to work here,' I said. 'She always says how nice it was.'

The demeanour of the two women altered at once. They relaxed, even preened themselves a little. 'Oh? What was her name?' the older one asked.

In the name o' the Kingdom o' Heaven, a pit was opening at my feet. My mother was Mrs. Robertson but what was her name before she married? What was her Christian name even? There was no answer on the blank screen of fourteen years of non-attachment, fourteen years of non-communication. I ignored the question and said in a dreamy thoughtful voice: 'She often talks about the lovely bronzes in your dining-room. I think she likes the ones on the mantelpiece the best. Two lovely ones of men with horses, she says they are.'

They were actually smiling at one another, self-satisfied, tight little smiles, as if they were all that could be spared from a meagre store and I began to feel the heady sense of inspiration that came to me when I was lying myself and some of my colleagues out of some trouble with old Cock at school, the inspiration that came at the point when I could see that I was succeeding.

'Would you like to see the dining-room, Jeanie?' the old one asked.

Jeanie! It was spoken with an indulgent patronage that assured me that I could play these old women as I chose.

'Yes, please, Miss Simpson.'

'Yes, please, *madam*,' she corrected me. 'Come, Jeanie.'

They rose to their feet and led the way out of the room, across the hall to another door. I paused beside the hideous Iron Man, looked around me and said: 'I think this house is just lovely, honest I do. And Laurelbank is such a lovely name.'

I was aware that, in the parlance of my school-fellows, I was now 'going it'. I could almost feel about me their taut-held breath as on the occasions when I began to go it with old

Cock, could almost feel their fear that I would go it too far, but my school-fellows had no conception of the artist under inspiration, the artist so 'in it' that she had the certainty of never putting a foot wrong.

The two women had paused in the hall to listen to my artless admiration and I went on: 'It's so much nicer to have an address that's a name and not just a number, like Number Three Railway Terrace. My granny's house has a name, Lilac Cottage, down in the Village ye know.' Some instinct told me that the snobbery connected with the Village extended to Lochview Crescent and this instinct was correct. The old one looked more pleased than ever, opened a door and said: 'This way, Jeanie. This is the dining-room.' There was another clutter of furniture, including a table that would have extended from the sink at one end of Number Three Railway Terrace to the aspidistra at the other and at each end of the mantel were two iron men, naked except for some strategically placed ivy leaves, who were trying, without much success, to control two rearing iron horses. I was standing looking up at them, hoping that my silence would be taken for rapt admiration, while I thought what fun it would be, in the end, to tell these two old women what they could do with their horrible house and their post as housetablemaid when, from behind me, came the voice of the younger woman, speaking for the first time.

'*I* know who the mother was, Bessie,' she said on a note of triumph. It took me a few seconds to realize that the impersonal 'the mother' she was speaking of was my own mother. 'It was Ada, Ada Bain, that one we got from the orphanage. *She* married a Villager. Don't you remember how surprised everybody was?'

They discussed the matter in an off-hand impersonal way, as if my mother and I were of no significance, but as if it were a satisfaction to themselves to have catalogued us, before the old one turned to me again.

'Is that right?' she asked. 'Ada Bain is your mother and your father is a Villager, Jeanie?'

'My father was killed at the war,' I said dully.

'I see.'

But she did not 'see'. She did not see that, for me, the knowledge, thrust upon me so suddenly, that my mother had been a nameless charity child was a stunning blow and at the same time a blinding revelation that explained more about my mother's nature than my mind could assimilate. I wanted to run away from this horrible airless house and all its iron men and all its blindness to people and their feelings but my legs felt weak and there was nowhere to go. Almost without being aware of it, I found myself engaged to come into the service of the Misses Simpson on the first Monday of July, at a salary of twenty shillings a month, with an evening free from four to ten each week and a Sunday evening free each month.

In a daze, I left the house, shown out through the back door by the fat woman and when I came up from the basement on to the gravel, I paused close to some dense bushes beside the drive to collect myself. Inside my head, there was this great lump of unassimilated knowledge about my mother, a huge, prison-like rectangular block of grey stone, that was my mental image of the orphanage Down-the-line that I had never seen. When my brain could set to work and grind down this lump, when thought could wash over and around it and melt it down, I would know a great deal more about my mother, I felt but I could not set to work on the hard grey lump as yet, in this strange place, dressed in my Sunday clothes. I began to walk round the house towards the gate, pushing the lump away to the back of my mind, thinking instead about the two old women in the big stuffy house. It might be amusing to work there, reading all their books without their knowing I was doing it.

Beside the corner of the drive, there was a bed of rose bushes and on one of them a pretty pink bud. Quickly I nipped it off and slipped it into the pocket of my coat. That old woman was not going to make me call her 'madam' without paying for it in some way. I did not want to go home, to face my mother until I had become more accustomed to the lump of new knowledge inside my head, but where could I go, all dressed up like this in my Sunday clothes? I thought of visiting my granny, but that did not feel right either. The lump inside my head was so new that it was possible her wise old eyes might notice it.

At the corner where the Crescent met the road to the town, I took the rosebud from my pocket and put it in my buttonhole, then strolled down the hill, pretending to be a Lochview lady on her way to the station, going Down-the-line to buy a new hat but I soon decided that this was silly. Lochview ladies did not walk to the station. They went Down-the-line and to Glasgow by car. Coming round the next corner of the road, with a hedge on one side and the Castle wall on the other, the main part of the town came into view, lying in its hollow below a faint blue mist of smoke from the household fires. It looked more than anything, I thought, like the heap of discarded boxes in the backyard of the Co-op. The boxes that were Railway Terrace and Tramway Buildings had black holes in their tops where some of the slates had slipped off, the tips at the Gas Works were like heaps of ashes beside the rusty tin cans of the gas-holders and the railway and tramway lines were like the lengths of tin tape that came round the orange boxes. It was one large heap of dilapidation and decay. 'Change and decay in all around I see—' came the words inside my head and singing the tune of the hymn I came skipping down the hill, stopping only when I came to the place where the pavement and the houses began, in case anyone seeing me might think that I was going religion-daft like Kingdom Come the Trammie.

I now began to walk decorously along, pretending that I was going to church on Sunday. When I reached the church door, people all dressed up with flowers in their buttonholes were beginning to arrive for the wedding, but neither old Beery-belly nor the scramble children were there as yet. For scrambles, we had learned that to arrive in the middle of the last bit of singing was time enough. A motor car, with three giggling women and three red-faced men who had not waited till after the wedding to have a drink, stopped as I reached the church door and naturally I paused to look at them as they got out of the car and went in. A man came out and gave them all pieces of white paper, like two leaves out of a book, so I held out my hand and he gave me one too. But then, he stood aside and gave me a gentle push into the church, seeming to think that I had come in the motor car with the other people. Well, being all dressed up anyway, a flower in my buttonhole and everything, I might as well have a look at this wedding, for I had never been to one before, so I followed the six people and sat at the end of a pew.

It was all very dull and went on for a very long time. I had had no idea that there was all this palaver before two people could go to bed and do That together but the white paper that the man at the door had given me was quite interesting. It told all the psalms and hymns that were to be sung during the ceremony and there was one hymn that was not my favourite but which seemed to be much liked by old Poopit, Miss Miller and Lewie Leadpipe. We had it every Sunday that old Poopit stood up again after the sermon and did the thing known as 'calling banns', which was telling you about people who were going to get married, although why their names had to be droned out in church I did not understand.

> *O Perfect Love, all human thought transcending,*
> *Lowly we kneel in prayer before Thy throne,*
> *That theirs may be the love that knows no ending*
> *Whom Thou forever more dost join in one.*

However, when it came to singing it, I sang it with the rest and it was the last one, thank goodness. When it was over, there was the benediction, then Miss Miller made that movement as of rolling up her sleeves, Lewie Leadpipe began to pump like fury and the organ started to lumber out that tune that made you think of an elephant trying to dance.

We had to wait in the church until the bride and bridegroom had gone out and then you could hear the noise of the scramble going on. When I came out, the red-faced man who had shared my pew threw another lot of half-pennies on to the pavement so I stood in the church porch, waiting till the scrambling was over, not wishing to be hurled down among the herring scales in my Sunday clothes. After all the people had come out of the church and had gone away and two of the bigger boys were having a fight about a halfpenny that they had rescued from the gutter drain, Maggie Graham saw me, saw my buttonhole and my hymn paper in my gloved hand.

'Jeanie Robertson,' she said, 'were you in it at that weddin'—in it in the very kirk?'

'Aye.'

'Ye said ye were goin' up Lochview after a job!'

'I was only coddin' ye.'

'But ye don't *ken* they folk that got mairrit!'

'What about it?' I boasted. 'I just came along in my Sunday coat and went in. The big softie at the door gave me this—' I brandished the hymn paper '—and in I went.'

'Jeanie Robertson! Here, Lizzie, Aggie, Teenie, d'ye ken what Jeanie Robertson did? She dressed hersel' up an' went right into the kirk to that weddin'. She was right in it!'

Already the rectangular lump inside my head felt less sharp as I began to count my blessings. I had escaped the shirt factory and old Pillans and I was now the heroine of the girls of the entire tribe for nobody, ever before, had thought of going uninvited to a fashionable wedding.

This being a Saturday, my mother was going back to the

Secondhand after tea, for Saturday evenings were always busy, some people selling household articles because the pay packet was already in the pub, some buying household articles before the pay packet was spent.

'And you're not going out raking about the-night,' she told me as I cleared the tea-table. 'Ye'll get ben there an' get on with the mangling.'

I wished that on this one evening she had been less belliger-ent, that she had given me a little time to imagine what it was like to have been an abandoned orphan. Already I felt that I understood some of her desperate need to improve her circum-stances, to be 'somebody in the world' and I wanted to make her aware of my understanding. But there were no words—it would take time to find them—and in the meantime her cold hardness, her keenness to return to the Secondhand and begin the horrid work of the evening made me angry.

'You go an' boil your can!' I told her. 'I've been up Loch-view an' I've got a job an' from now on you can do your own damn mangling.'

'Jeanie Robertson, of all the vulgar ungrateful—'

'Ach, shut your face!'

'Now, you listen to me. What is this job? I'm your mother an' I've a right—'

'It's tablemaid at Laurelbank, like you were.'

'Tablemaid? Laurelbank?' Wide-eyed and weak, she leaned her back against the coal bunker. 'But who spoke for ye?'

'Spoke for me?' Oh, she meant the letter I should have had from old Cock or old Poopit. 'I don't need speaking for. I can speak for myself. And who would speak for me any-way? Old Pillans?' and with this parting shot, I went out into the street to see what was doing.

At first, it was much like any other Saturday night in Lochfoot. A cloud of greasy blue smoke and the usual smell were issuing from the door of the fish and chip shop. On the

192

pavement outside the Secondhand, there was a woman with a roll of linoleum and another with an iron kettle, waiting for my mother to open up for business and down the other way from Railway Terrace Corner, Kingdom Come was taking up his position for an evening of singing and preaching outside the pub.

Down past Kingdom Come, on the road up from Pillans's corner, there was a sudden noise of horses' hooves on the road, accompanied by much singing and shouting and a cavalcade of five tinkers' floats came rattling along, swept past me round the corner into the Terrace backyard and along at full tilt through the forest of clothes poles to the far end. Suddenly, too, all the members of the child tribe were around me and somebody was shouting: 'It's a Tinkers' weddin'. Willie Cameron's been away an' got mairrit an' that's him an' his wife hame. Come on!'

And now all of us were galloping along the yard to the far end where Sandy was already blowing up his pipes while Kitchener looked out of his window, twitching his ears in anticipation.

It was much better than the wedding in the church that afternoon. The bride's clan had brought her and her groom back to her new home in fine style. She came from a camp away Down-the-line, it was said and in their carts her relatives had brought ample supplies for what was probably the second wedding feast. Each of the five floats had its quota of whisky, its bundle of hay for its horse, its pairs of rabbits tied together by the hind legs and its sack of potatoes. We children helped to unyoke the horses and tether them to clothes-poles, helped to unload the floats and ended by fetching Hector's tin mug from the wash-house and hanging it round his neck by its string.

When the bridal pair were ensconced on the step at the close mouth with tin mugs of whisky in their hands, the rest of us began to dance to the music of Sandy's pipes and when we paused between reels to draw our breath while Sandy wet his whistle, Sandy's Mary or some other woman would come out with the roasted carcasses of a pair of rabbits which she would tear apart and distribute a leg here and a body there to all us guests. Naturally, on such an occasion, all enmity was forgotten and the MacPhee clan too were at the celebration and Katie MacPhee would come out with her apron full of baked potatoes in their skins, fresh out of the ashes of the fire. Hector, who knew that when the pipes played he must walk round on his hind legs with his tin mug, carried out his duty but, tonight, no pennies went into the mug. People tipped some whisky out of their bottles into it and when Hector found it a little heavy on his neck, he went over to Sandy who took the mug off by the string over Hector's head and drank the contents.

The fun was furious for a long time but, human nature being what it is, the Cameron—MacPhee enmity could not remain buried for ever, even at a wedding and as a reel came to an end out in the yard, we dancers became aware that all was not well within the two end houses of Railway Terrace, as an enamel basin came flying out through a window. The bride and groom sprang up from their step and went inside, followed by all the Tinker dancers from the yard. Sounds of a raging battle emerged from the houses while Kitchener, from his window, gave a high whinny of delight.

We of the child tribe, experts in survival, retired to safety behind the line of tethered visiting horses. It was one of the best fights ever seen in Lochfoot and Sandy's old Mary, armed with a frying pan, made mincemeat of the MacPhee women, hurling them out into the yard through their own kitchen window while the Cameron men evicted one MacPhee after another from the close mouth. Beery-belly and Macaroni arrived but they merely stood behind the horses and us children, took a long sad look at the battlefield and went away back to their police station.

The midsummer sky was misting over towards evening when the battle began to die down. Old Sandy took a drink from a nearby bottle and was beginning to blow up his pipes again while we children prepared to re-commence dancing when a long tongue of flame came licking out through the window of the Cameron kitchen. In less than five minutes, the whole end of Railway Terrace was ablaze and, fascinated, we watched the flames rise and begin to travel along the roof in one direction while, in the other direction, they reached out, trying to lick the gable of Tramway Buildings.

With splendid drunken unconcern, the Tinkers paid no attention to the fire. In the lurid unnatural light, they yoked the horses to their floats, loaded what few belongings were lying around and drove down to the end of the yard and out on to the street. This was merely a move to another place, welcomed in lives that had been made up of moves to another place. Those, such as the MacPhees, who had no transport, walked alongside and last in the procession came Kitchener, walking proudly in front of the Cameron float, his hooves spurning the hated concrete of the yard, while Mary held the reins and Sandy, his bagpipes across his knees, held Hector by his string collar with one hand and took a drink from a whisky bottle with the other.

Lochfoot had no fire brigade of its own and before the brigade arrived from Down-the-line, eight houses at the end of the Terrace had been destroyed, the four that the Camerons and MacPhees had occupied and the four vacant ones next door. In the small hours of the morning, the fire brigade went away, the crowd dispersed through the thin dark and my mother and Miss Miller retired to the close mouth to discuss the vulgarity of it all.

'I've never been up this late before,' confided wee Sammy Gardiner, who was beside me, holding my hand. I had suddenly remembered him earlier and had run down to bring him to the wedding. Probably not even the wildest child in Lochfoot had been up this late before, I thought but, before I took Sammy home, we went along to see the place where the end of the Terrace used to be. It was like Tom Telfer's rotten tooth that he had shown some of us in the playground once, a hollow shell of black decay.

We came back along the Terrace and I took Sammy down to his mother who, like everybody else, had been watching the fire. Then, when I came back along the pavement to our corner, I stood there and watched Kingdom Come the Trammie pass on his way home. While the fire had raged, lighting up the whole street, he had stayed at his post, calling upon the watching crowd to repent of their sins before the fires of Hell overtook them but, as usual, nobody had heeded him. Nobody ever heeded Kingdom Come but he did not seem to care. As he made his way home, he was still humming a hymn to himself.

Suddenly I felt a slithering movement near me and close to the wall. I drew hastily back and round the corner and Old Pillans passed by, a furtive blackness in the summer dark. Kingdom Come, along by the burned-out hole now, had begun to sing aloud:

> *Change and decay in all around I see;*
> *O Thou who changest not, abide with me.*

CHAPTER TEN

Onward! Christian soldiers,
Marching as to war—

EVER SINCE THE WAR ENDED in November of 1918, there had
been a series of sales of work, raffles and other money-
raising enterprises, because the townspeople were collecting
money to erect a war memorial. For over a year, this had
provided us older children with a new activity. We enjoyed
marching up to the doors of houses, near which we had
never been allowed to go before, ringing the bells boldly
and, instead of running jeering away, saying: 'Raffle tickets.
Tuppence. For the memorial.' It was a form of blackmail.
Very few citizens, tired as they were of raffles and of our
visits, had the courage to tell us to go away and shut their
doors without buying a ticket. Lochfoot had some sort of
distinction connected with the number of its men killed in
the war, but I do not remember precisely what this was,
whether the town contributed more men than any other
town of comparative size in Scotland or whether it was
Tramway Buildings that had more war orphans than any
other such building in Great Britain. The distinction was
something of this sort, however. It turned upon the number
of men killed.

When, in the spring of 1920, the memorial began to take
physical shape, naturally we maintained a strict watch over
this new feature of our territory, from the very first moment
when man began to knock a hole in the Castle wall, down
near the station, at almost precisely the place where the
steamie had breached the wall long ago. Having knocked
down about fifteen feet of wall, the men at once began to
rebuild round a recess into the Castle grounds which was

about twelve feet deep and very soon the Castle wall was as complete as ever, although it now looked as if some giant had taken a large roadside bite out of the Castle grounds. The Lochfoot *Leader*, in a long article, said that the Castle had graciously given to the town this magnificent site for the memorial, but when I thought of all the miles of Up-the-Burn and all the miles of woodland and all the acres of the Home Farm, the bite at the roadside did not seem to be so impressive. Still, it was the first time that I had ever known a bit to be taken out of the Castle wall and first bites are always flavoured with their own strangeness, excitement and satisfaction.

As time went on, a hole was dug in the ground of the recess and out of this there began to rise a thick four-sided pillar that tapered towards the top and was made of rough grey stone. On each of the four sides, the men made a panel of smooth mortar and on these four smooth parts, we understood, the names of the killed men were to appear. We went down every day to inspect progress until, one morning, we found the thing covered with a tarpaulin and no workmen near it, after which we lost interest and no wonder, for there was a new project afoot in the town. Suddenly, there were doings at the most unlikely place of all, old Pillans's place. It was at school dinner-hour that this news rose out of the ground and everybody went rushing helter-skelter along the road from the playground gates to the corner by the bridge, everybody except me, that is, for I came along behind with wee Sammy Gardiner at his own slow pace.

Ever since the day I had gone to the Village to tell my granny about my father being killed and she had said how hard it was that the Gardiners had two lameters in one family, a queer thing had been happening inside my head. Whenever there came news of doings and the child tribe began to run to the site, a picture of wee Sammy with his crutch, limping along, trying to keep up, would come into my head. If I did not stop running with the rest, the picture would change and

I would see wee Sammy dropping further and further behind, then giving up and leaning disconsolately against a wall or a fence and then, in the picture in my mind, the road would take a turn like a snake, blotting out wee Sammy from sight. This was unbearable and I would have to let the rest of the crowd run on while I went back to fetch him. That was why I had gone to fetch him for the Tinkers' wedding and that was why I held his hand while we watched the fire. Wee Sammy was all tangled up with my father being killed so that, even against my will, I seemed to be in it with him.

And now, inside my head, a new thing was happening. Every time I saw wee Sammy, I would find myself thinking of my mother. I longed to tell my mother that I knew about her being an orphan and I longed to comfort her, to tell her that she was not all alone any more, that I was in it with her and was grateful for how she had fed me, clothed me and kept me clean but there was no way of saying these things. There were no words and, this apart, she was withdrawing further and further into herself every day, as if she were making for herself a small isolating orphanage with high, forbidding grey walls. It was as if her mind were crippled, as wee Sammy's leg was and encased like Sammy's leg in a brace of steel, so that I could not get near to her or touch her. Unlike Sammy, she did not want to be helped, did not seem to feel that she needed help, so I gave the help to Sammy instead.

Thus, here I was, dawdling along a few yards in front of him, not speaking to him or looking as if he mattered, of course, but forming a sort of link between him and the running crowd away ahead of us. When, at last, Sammy and I arrived at the corner, I vented my exasperation at being last but one on the scene, as I always did on these occasions, by cuffing and kicking everyone, especially the younger ones of Sammy's age who were able-bodied, as I fought my way to a front place for myself and Sammy. After all, I was one of the big girls now, entitled to a front place at everything unless

I was a softie, which I was not and it was up to Sammy to follow me if he wanted to be in it. I was a 'big' girl in the sense that I was fourteen years old but that was all, for in stature I was about half the size of most of the other girls of my age but I could hold my own and a place for Sammy too, if he had the sense to follow me, which he had. I had always been distinguished as a liar but on my way up through the school I had also become known as a very wily and dirty fighter. I think my eel-catching had endowed me with a quickness of eyes, hands and feet that the other girls and many boys had never achieved.

And so I had very soon kicked, clawed and cuffed my way through the crowd and right up to the hole in Pillans's wall where the gate should have been and now, without looking round, I put a hand behind me, caught Sammy's crutch and pulled it and him round in front of me where he could have a ringside view. A lot of strange men with two lorries were in Pillans's yard, loading all the old iron and rubbish and even as we watched, one lorry was filled and we heard the foreman tell the driver to get along down to the station and get the stuff loaded on to the railway. By the next day, the area that surrounded the house was completely clear and the morning after that, we were all late for school with the excitement of it for, in the yard, there was a lorry that had 'Murray & Jamieson, Housebuilding Contractors, Strichen Street, Ibrox' written along the side of it and from this a gang of men were unloading wood, tools, slates and all sorts of things.

'Old Pillans is getting his old den all sorted up,' I said to my mother at dinner-time, for I liked to keep before her my disapproval of her working at the Secondhand by making a reference now and then to her employer.

'Den!' she said. 'Mr. Pillans's house is the best house in Lochfoot. And its name is Castleside.'

Castleside! Imagine old Pillans having an address that was not just a number but a name! You could have knocked me down with a feather. Castleside my backside, I thought but I was silent while my mother continued: 'Castleside Farm, it used to be called long ago. That house is a valuable antique, that's what it is. Mr. Pillans knows a good thing when he sees it, like the clock that Trammie woman brought into the shop last Saturday. Fifteen bob he gave her for it and he got fifty-seven pound ten for it from a dealer in Glasgow. Mr. Pillans fairly knows what's what. When he's done with Castleside, it'll be the best house in Lochfoot, aye, the best house for miles round about. You'll see.'

I did not say any more in our house about what was going on down at Pillans's place although I watched the progress there along with my fellows. There was no doubt that, day by day, the house became more and more impressive and when all the windows which had been boarded over were glazed and new glass put into the little fan-shaped window above the new, shiny black front door, it was impossible to think of it any more as 'old Pillans's place'. It was quite definitely Castleside, with a name and a dignity of its own and there was something that made you feel sick in the thought that it belonged to old Pillans, that these white newly harled walls and regular oblong windows framed in black on the white were to conceal him and his slimy evil machinations. The boarded-up old ruin had been an appropriate setting for him but that he should live in this lovely house was an indecency and a desecration.

When the first novelty of the repairs wore off, the boys of the tribe lost interest but we girls continued to give Castleside our attention. The other girls did not seem to object as much as I did to old Pillans living in it but then they were not as involved with him as I felt myself to be. After all, their mothers did not work for him. As the work went on and the house emerged in its true dignity which had been in abeyance for so long, I became more and more uneasy. There was something incongruous in old Pillans spending all this money, as incongruous and unnatural as if the waters of the Burn had suddenly begun to flow up-hill to the Dam. Pillans gathered money in with his long snaky tentacles, but he did not expend it on the beautifying of a house or on anything else.

The work on the house had begun early in the year and by the beginning of June, the workmen had finished. We watched them load all their tools and equipment into their lorries and drive away, while the house looked out across the tidy yard to us, standing in a row behind the new gate in the mended wall, the new glass of the windows like patient thoughtful eyes. That evening at tea-time, my mother was wearing her most efficient business-woman air as she said: 'There'll be no dinner here the morn. Ye'll come to Castleside for your dinner.'

I felt my temper rise but I was wary. If I were careful, I might discover why the waters of the Burn seemed to be flowing up-hill to the Dam.

'Castleside?' I repeated.

'The furniture's coming down from Glasgow the morn an' I am to see it brought in.' From the top of the coal bunker, she picked up a sheaf of papers and waved it importantly under my nose.

'This is the list. I'll be down there all day for the next three days,' she said while I read at the top of the first sheet of paper 'Six mahogany sideboards'.

'Six mahogany sideboards!' I squeaked. 'Sideboards if you please! What does old Pillans want with six sideboards?'

She slammed the papers face downwards on the coal bunker. 'That's not for you to read, you impudent inquisitive brat! These papers are private.'

'He must be hell of a fond of his ugly face if he needs *six* sideboard mirrors to see it in,' I said unrepentantly.

Miss Miller's sideboard had a mirror at the back and I thought that all sideboards were like this. 'I just happened to notice her passing in the sideboard mirror,' was one of Miss Miller's refined ways of explaining that she had been spying on her neighbours. As I hoped, my cheek about old Pillans drew my mother out.

'You hold your cheeky tongue,' she told me. 'You've no idea of what's what. Castleside is to be a shop, a very high-class antique shop.'

'A shop?' I was amazed but relieved. The waters of the Burn were still flowing downhill after all.

'I must say that Mr. Pillans can fairly see in front of him,' my mother was continuing. 'All the old-fashioned furniture is going to come back into fashion, he says, and he has a warehouse full of it up in Glasgow. He's been buying it in for years and keeping only the very best and that's what's coming down to Castleside,' she ended triumphantly.

'He's off his bloody chump,' I said emphatically, but knowing all the time that I was a frightened angry child, shouting in the dark. Old Pillans was not off his chump. He was sane in a manner and degree in which no man should be allowed to be sane.

'Who in Lochfoot's going to buy old-fashioned sideboards? Old Lewie Leadpipe?' I stormed but my mother blandly took no notice of my infantile noise.

'The age o' the motor car is here,' she said sententiously, obviously quoting from her mentor. 'Rich folk drive out here at weekends and come down to the Arms from Glasgow and that. Old-fashioned furniture will sell better when seen in an old-fashioned setting, Mr. Pillans says and he knows how many beans make five in that way.'

I was so overcome that I did not bother to have the last word but began to eat my scanty meal in silence.

I had made up my mind that I would go without dinner the next day rather than eat it at old Pillans's place but at forenoon interval, a large pantechnicon was seen in the yard in front of Castleside and we all stood up on the playground wall, looking through the railings and up the road.

'Isn't that your ma at the door?' one of the girls asked me.

'Aye.' I was ashamed. 'She's checking in the furniture an' stuff.'

'Gosh, I wish I was her. I'll bet ye it's lovely. My ma says old Pillans is rotten wi' money. Here, Jeanie, can ye no' go in there at dinner-time an' tell us what's going on?'

'Easy,' I said grandly. 'I'm to go there for my dinner anyway.'

'Aren't ye the lucky one?'

The house consisted of a ground floor, a first floor and an attic floor. A kitchen, wash-house and coal-house jutted out in a small wing at the back of the ground floor and in addition to this there were four large square rooms on this level and another four rooms of similar size on the floor above. I had never been inside a house so huge, except Laurelbank and this one was much more interesting. It had two staircases. From the front hall, an elegant staircase rose in a graceful curve to the floor above and from the scullery a wooden near-ladder went at a sharpish angle straight up to the attics. It was when I explored the kitchen and attics that I realized that this house was a curious replica of Number Three Railway Terrace. Only the hall, the front staircase and the eight main rooms had been decorated and only the front and sides of the outside of the house had been repaired. The back of the house, which could be seen only from the yards of the shops and the pub, was as dilapidated as ever and the kitchen, back staircase and attics were filthy and sour-smelling, with paper and plaster falling from the ceilings and walls. Just as the parlour at Railway Terrace held nothing but the aspidistra and the curtains at the window and later the mangle, this house had eight rooms, a hall and a staircase to impress the visiting public. The kitchen and attics were still the den of old Pillans.

Just as my mother and I finished our dinner of cold sausage and potatoes, another pantechnicon arrived and my mother told me to get back to school, but I did not go. While she busied herself with her lists, I went up to have a proper look at the attics. Before dinner, I had reached only the top of the narrow wooden stairs before I had been called back. There were four attic rooms with sloping ceilings but with large dormer windows, the two front rooms looking grievously shamed by the sun that shone in through the new window-frames and glass on this side. They were empty of everything except dirt and spiders and so was one of the back rooms but the other set me back on my heels when I opened the door. It had a double bedstead, made of iron like the one in our kitchen, which was a jumble of frayed dirty blankets. It had an old armchair which was upholstered in brown material very like that on my old chairbed. It had two joiner-made kists of plain wood and it had its own version of the Iron Man, in the form of a stuffed stag's head hanging on the wall, its glassy eyes staring in death while a pair of old Pillans's trousers hung by their braces from one of the points of its spread antlers. I looked at it all from the doorway, even the gas ring, tin kettle and cup with no handle under a shelf in a corner, then fled downstairs, let myself out through the back door and ran back to the playground.

My mother worked like a slave in that house. The carpets, china, furniture, silver, glass, bric-à-brac which had been lying in storage for years were all filthy and she did not rest until all met with her meticulous standards of cleanliness. There was something maniacal in the way she worked and partly out of an uncanny fear for her, partly out of a desire to help her in any way I could, partly out of curiosity, I would go down there some evenings with her. I had never seen such furniture as came out of those pantechnicons. During the day, my mother would wash the wood carefully with soap and water and in the evenings, when it was dry, I would be set to polish it. Under the duster, it would begin to glow wine-red, deep chestnut and pale gold, so that I would forget that it belonged to old Pillans and caress it with my dusters for its own sake. But then my mother would inspect my finished work, put her head on one side and say: 'I bet you *that* will fetch more than *one* twenty pound!' and I would say: 'To blazes! I'm off out to play,' throw my dusters in a heap and run away to join my friends round the door of the pub while my mother called me in vain to come back.

Nevertheless, I spent quite a lot of time down at Castleside with her but not at any time did I see old Pillans down there. It seemed that he was going to Glasgow early in the mornings and returning only late at night.

'Mr. Pillans is a very busy man,' my mother explained, 'with all the things he has on hand.'

'What things?'

'Arranging for all the buying and selling and everything.'

'I suppose he'll be buying up the Castle next,' I said scornfully.

It was now public knowledge that the Castle was to be sold and there were posters in the town announcing the auction of the furniture early in July.

'Not the Castle itself,' my mother told me patronizingly, 'but he will have some of his men at the sale of the furniture.'

'Some of his men?'

My mother spoke now in her talking-to-herself voice. 'Mr. Pillans doesn't go to sales himself. He has men to do that for him. Mr. Pillans is a very private sort of gentleman.'

'There's nothing private about him when he's buying for the Secondhand on Saturday nights!' I burst forth.

'That is different,' she told me. 'As he says, he is quite sentimental about the Secondhand. It was the first business he ever had, you see.'

After one of these discussions, I would swear to myself that I would never lift another duster for the good of Pillans but, somehow because of my mother, my resolve would break down and I would go back to help her at Castleside. Her whole being was concentrated on bringing these eight rooms full of furniture to the standard of perfection that she wanted, so that she forgot about our home at Railway Terrace. We slept there and had porridge there in the mornings but that was all now and our kitchen was taking on the aspect of Pillans's squalid attic. Our beds were never made and the room was never swept unless I did these things and when I did them, my mother did not even notice. At night, she was too tired and in the morning she was in too much of a hurry to get down to Castleside.

Like everything else, however, the work among the furniture, silver and china at last came to an end. The orgy of cleaning had lasted, probably for only about two weeks but, to me, it had seemed to be a long time because of the change in my mother in the course of it. She now seemed to wear openly and all the time the avid scheming look that used to appear on her face only on Saturday nights when she bent, secret and unseen, as she thought, over her kist with the little bags of coins and bundles of notes.

On our last evening at Castleside, she was washing china and glass at the kitchen sink and I had been set to polish a small mahogany bureau.

'I washed the outside of it,' she said, 'but I hadn't time to dust the inside. Mind and take all the drawers out and dust them thorough. That bottom drawer doesn't go in right. There must be dirt in the runners.'

She went away to her china and I set to work, taking the bureau apart on the dust sheet that lay on the hall floor. It had four long drawers under a fold-down flap and in the part above the flap it had six little drawers and a lot of pigeon-holes. When I pulled out the last of these little drawers, a piece of folded paper was stuck to the bottom of it and on opening this I read: '18th January, 1901. My dearest brother Charles, for my writing lesson today I have copied this hymn to comfort you at the War. Onward! Christian soldiers, Marching as to war, with the Cross of Jesus going on before. I hope that you will come home soon. The new gardener's cat has had five kittens. Your loving sister Jean.'

It took me a little time to realize that this was a letter, written long ago, by a girl to her brother but it took me no time at all to decide that this was one thing that old Pillans would never touch. I would protect this letter written by my long-ago namesake from his slimy hands and I slipped the paper up the leg of my knickers as I began to hum 'Onward! Christian soldiers' and dust all the little drawers and pigeon-holes. This hymn, as it chanced, was the order of the day at school at that time.

Having polished all the wood inside the top part of the bureau, I closed the flap and began to pull out the four long drawers and to dust out the recesses in which they ran. I did this with an Up-the-Burn thrill of exploration, for there might be yet another concealed letter, but I brought forth nothing other than the clotted dust of years until I came to the bottom recess.

Here, jammed at the back, there was something quite large which I could feel with my fingers, but I could not get it out because the recess was as deep as the length of my arm from finger-tips to shoulder. With persistence, I pressed and prodded until, at last, with a little jerk it yielded and I drew out a little book in a faded greenish-grey cover. '*Cranford*' said the black lettering on the front 'by Mrs. Gaskell' and inside on the first page, in faded ink, 'To Jean, from her loving brother Charles. 4th May, 1900.' I stared down at the first real present I had ever had and took the book to myself at once.

I heard my mother's footsteps approaching and her voice: 'Are you getting on with that polishing?' so I pushed the book up the other leg of my knickers and began to dust the drawer, but I was jubilant. I felt as if this long-ago Charles were truly my loving brother who had given me a present and for the first time in my life, I owned a book, a book not lent by the school or pinched from the Penny Library or the Railway Terrace book cases.

When I had finished with the bureau, my mother and I carried the shell of it between us into the place that she had designated for it in one of the rooms, then we put the four long drawers into it and I gave it a final rub all over with my duster.

'I must say,' said my mother, 'that when ye do a thing ye make a good job of it. Ye've been a real help down here, Jeanie.'

These were the most civil words I could ever remember my mother speaking to me and when I was in my chairbed that night, a strange thought came into the inside of my head. I had a book of my own, safely concealed in the wash-house which was never used now because the frost had cracked the boiler and my mother had praised me for the first time in my life but the root circumstance of these good happenings was that evil old snake, Pillans.

During the latter part of that month of June, 1920, however, there was not much time for thought or for following the long tortuous chain of circumstance leading to circumstance. There was too much doing. I was in the last fortnight of my school-days and soon it would be Prize Day, a Friday when the Villagers would take all the prizes as usual and, on the following Monday, I would be leaving home to start work at Laurelbank. But on the Saturday between these two events, there was to be an event of a kind hitherto unknown in Lochfoot, an event to which we children referred as the 'Unavailing'.

Our derogatory adjective 'old' was merited by old Cock our schoolmaster on grounds of age. He had been an old man ever since I went to school in 1911 and by 1920 he was very much older than a mere nine years of calendar time could justify. He was a much respected member of the adult community, an elder of the church and a member of the Town Council but to the child tribe, especially to the thirteen- and fourteen-year-olds who sat in his Top Classroom, he was a figure of fun with no armour against us except his broad leather strap, fringed at the tip, which he was now hardly strong enough to wield to real effect. He had always had a small defect of speech, which became more marked as he grew older, in that he could not pronounce certain consecutive consonants without inserting a hesitant little 'ah' sound between them, very much as Antonio, the fish and chip man, tended to end his words with an Italianate vowel.

'Tom a Telfer,' old Cock would say, 'I have a given years of a my life to make a you a literate Christian a but to no avail. I wash a my hands of you.'

He washed his hands of Tom Telfer about a dozen times each day. When we remembered, we referred to our headmaster as 'Old a Cock'. Like most of our teachers, the notable exception being Miss Gibson, who made sure that we understood the meaning of the hymn that began: 'When from Egypt's house of bondage,' old Cock was not given to explanations and most of our learning in his class was done by rote. The words 'But, sir, I thought——' were to old Cock like a red rag to a rather weary bull. 'You are not here to think,' he would say, reaching for his strap. Our world, therefore, was a world of dumb acceptance until the point of rebellion was reached, a world in which the words 'War Memorial' had no meaning for us except the truncated pillar that had been erected by the roadside. We had taken an interest in it because it was something new and different but now we became even more interested when we came to understand that we were to be personally involved with it.

'This a school,' said old Cock one morning, 'has a been asked by the War a Memorial Committee to supply a choir for the Un a veiling.' In our understanding of this pronouncement, we all failed to take into account old Cock's peculiarity of speech. 'Unveiling' was a word that we had not heard before and the coming ceremony was referred to by all of us as the 'Un-a-veiling' and in my own mind, furthermore, it was spelled 'unavailing'. To me, a veil was an item of female dress, as worn to church by that uppish Miss Miller, as if she were one of the toffs from Lochview Crescent instead of just a retired railway guard's old maid sister and I had never thought of Miss Miller being 'unveiled' while sitting at the organ. But I was familiar with the word 'avail', for the phrase 'to no avail' fell from old Cock's lips more and more frequently while there was also the hymn which said: 'What though the struggle naught availeth.' We were all, therefore, in the latter part of June, 1920, looking forward to the Unavailing of the War Memorial and we felt that, because of the choir drawn from the school, that we were very much in it.

We had the idea that it would be an enjoyable function, having heard a rumour that the town's brass band was to take part but, above all, it was connected with the war, that time of such colourful memory for all of us, when Doris and her friends were at the Arms, the Belgies at the Paddies and there had been the dancing in the station yard and the lively fights among the soldiers at the pub doors. Finally, the Unavailing was presenting us with an opportunity that had never come our way before, in that we of the Top Class, even Tom Telfer of no avail, who had a good singing voice, were to contribute to the programme by singing 'Onward! Christian soldiers' under the baton of old Cock.

He divided us into sopranos, altos, tenors and basses and there was rehearsal after rehearsal, culminating in the great day when we were marched in twos right through the town to the memorial. There, with much fuss and importance, old Cock, old Beery-belly and the War Memorial Committee decided that the forty-odd of us were to stand in a four-row semicircle in a certain place on the great day and old Cock threatened with terrible retribution anyone who did not remember his exact spot on the pavement and the roadway.

I was a little worried. A tramline went along under my feet and I wondered if it would be legitimate to get out of the way of an oncoming tramcar, until somebody told me that, on the great day itself, even the clanging trams would be halted.

The memorial was now finished. It was about twice the height it had been when we had last seen the stone pillar uncovered but now it was covered all the time by a big tarpaulin that hung down round it like a tent from its pointed top and an iron railing with a gate in it had been erected along the front of the recess where it stood, separating it from the roadway. Thus the memorial was enclosed on three sides by Castle wall and on the fourth by an iron railing, like Lochfoot itself, when you thought about it.

Although the memorial was now finished and the Unavailing was soon to take place, the work of construction was not completely paid for and under the auspices of the War Memorial Committee, there broke out a new rash of sales of work, concerts and raffle tickets to be sold. Ever since the raising of funds for the memorial began, my granny had steadfastly refused to contribute a penny and I shall never forget my horrified astonishment when I tried to sell her a twopenny raffle ticket.

'No, Jean,' she said in her quiet way. 'I have better things to do with my money than buy raffle tickets for war memorials as they call them.'

They were words more likely to be spoken by my mother than by my granny but they were spoken in my granny's quiet voice and I pondered them. Even my mother and Miss Miller bought raffle tickets for the memorial because it was vulgar not to but my granny would not buy raffle tickets and whatever my granny was, I was certain that she was not vulgar. Then, one day, wee Sammy came to school wearing a new navy-blue jersey and I said: 'You're not half a swank the-day, Sammy. Have yer folk come into a fortune?' for this was how, traditionally, one remarked upon any new garment. But

Sammy did not give me the traditional reply of: 'Ach, away an' boil your can.' In spite of my best efforts, Sammy was not tribally educated. Indeed, he did not seem to be educable in its customs and sayings and now he looked up at me in his confiding trusting way and said: 'I got it from your granny, Jeanie. She bought new wool and knitted it for me.'

For a moment, I was angry and jealous. My granny had never bought new wool to knit anything for me but then I remembered her saying, after my father was killed, that there was 'nothing coming over' my mother.

'She'll have a pension for your father,' she told me, 'and he aye gave her all he ever made, except the shilling or two he drank and smoked and she has been careful with what she had. She is very saving, your mother.' After some further thought, I understood why my granny did not buy raffle tickets. She preferred to contribute her spare pennies to the Gardiner household, in the way of extras for delicate legless Mr. Gardiner and wool for jerseys for wee Sammy.

When the new rash of raffle tickets broke out, old Cock had the usual pile of ticket books on his desk one Friday afternoon, weighted down by his leather strap and when we had done our final rehearsal of 'Onward! Christian soldiers' for the week, he got ready to hand them out. He would call the boys and girls out one by one, giving them the books and writing down the numbers of the tickets they contained, along with the name of the seller, on a sheet of paper.

'Jeanie Robertson!' he called, right at the start.

'No, sir,' I said, before I had thought about it, even.

'*What* did you say?' he asked, his hand reaching automatically for the strap.

'No, sir,' I repeated and added into the breathless hush that held the classroom: 'I am not going to sell any more raffle tickets.'

'Come out here at once!' he bellowed and, very frightened, I went out to stand by his high desk. 'So *this* is all a you think

213

of the gallant a men who died a to save you——' he began and went on to make a long speech but I did not listen.

When he had talked himself out, he picked up a book of tickets and held it towards me, but I would not take it. I was so frightened, already feeling the sting of the fringed strap on both palms, that I could hardly speak but I had adopted this course and I was not going to retract in front of the whole Top Class which was poised on a knife-edge of silence, ready to drop into admiration if I won, scorn if I lost.

'I am not going to sell them and you can't make me,' I said and added a belated 'sir' so that, at least, he could not leather me for not conforming to school discipline.

'Stand over there,' he told me, obviously playing for time and called: 'Isa Beattie!'

'No, sir,' said Isa.

'Tom Telfer!' the name was an angry shout.

'No, sir,' said Tom nearly as loudly.

In the end, purple in the face, old Cock shouted 'Dismiss!' and we all clattered out into the playground, leaving him with his pile of raffle tickets.

The last fortnight of June was always characterized by some act of defiance against old Cock by a pupil or pupils who were about to leave school for good but the act, as a rule, was perpetrated by a boy, who usually paid the penalty of a sound leathering. My act of defiance was regarded by the Top Class as divinely inspired because the defiance had related to a matter that was outside of the school curriculum. For once, we had reduced the authority of old Cock to complete impotence and instinctively we were aware of that elemental law of war which lays down that the moment a breach has been made in the enemy defence, that is the moment for strong attack.

In an attempt to wreak vengeance upon us the next day, old Cock called Tom Telfer out to be thrashed for some very minor offence and Tom refused to leave his seat, whereupon two of the other older boys, in support of Tom, threw their inkwells full of ink at our headmaster, while they shouted: 'Shove your belt up your arse, old Cock!' At this point in an occurrence the like of which Lochfoot school had never seen before, Tom Telfer and his two supporters rushed out into the middle of the floor, gripped in the madness of a sortie up Lochview and were about to lay violent hands upon old Cock who was backing away before their concerted onslaught. Perhaps because of excitement, perhaps through the instinct of self-preservation which always came to our lawless aid, suddenly the other thirty-seven or so of us were singing, stamping our feet in time to the tune:

> *Onward! Christian soldiers*
> *Marching as to war—*

To the other teachers in the building, this would sound like one more rehearsal of our contribution to the Unavailing and while it released our pent-up excitement, it would also prevent the second master from coming to old Cock's aid or being a witness to his assault if it took place.

But Tom and his supporters did not make the threatened assault on the person of the headmaster. Instead, they let their arms drop to their sides and grinning as they surrounded the terrified old Cock, they joined in as we embarked on the second verse:

> *At the sign of triumph,*
> *Satan's legions flee;*
> *On then Christian soldiers,*
> *On to victory!*
> *Hell's foundations quiver*
> *At the shout of praise;*
> *Brothers, lift your voices,*
> *Loud your anthems raise.*

Old Cock, who had been purple with fury, was now pale as

he made a tentative movement in the direction of the door. Tom and his two supporters, smiling their scorn, parted their ranks to let him through while they went on singing the chorus with the rest of us:

Onward! Christian soldiers—

It was a glorious finish to what we regarded as nine years of servitude, punctuated by not a little brutal injustice and my fellows paid me due regard as the pebble that started the avalanche. When they deferred to me in this way, I would wonder sometimes why I had refused to sell the raffle tickets for I had enjoyed selling them and would still enjoy selling them, with the ringing of forbidden doorbells and all that it entailed. The refusal was all bound up with my granny, wee Sammy and in a dim incomprehensible way with the memory of my father, standing in the doorway of our house in a dirty kilt and it was bound up with many other things. It was all dim and shadowy but it also had a firm rightness in my mind. All the reasons for the refusal meshed together into rightness in the way that the four different tunes, sung together by the four different sections of our class, meshed together into one tune of 'Onward! Christian soldiers'.

CHAPTER ELEVEN

O Perfect Love—

TOWARDS THE END OF JUNE, after the rebellion when old Cock lost control of the Top Class, I plunked school very frequently, partly because it was the correct thing for us victorious fourteen-year-olds to do, partly because I was acutely anxious about my mother.

Since we had completed the cleaning and the arranging of the furniture at Castleside, she had drawn away into herself, her face secretive, her eyes lowered, as if she were entirely concentrated on some scheme inside her head. She never wore, nowadays, that brisk, efficient businesslike air that she had been wont to put on when something of profit had been doing at the Secondhand and she did not talk in that admiring way, as if to herself, about old Pillans any more. She went her way silently and unobtrusively, but it seemed to me that there was more than silent unobtrusiveness. Her manner was verging on the furtive secrecy that, until now, had been peculiar to old Pillans himself.

Castleside lay locked and quiet as we had left it on the evening when we finished the cleaning, when I had come home with that other Jean's letter and her copy of *Cranford* in the legs of my knickers. Pillans was spending the nights there, I knew, creeping around the house and in through the back door in his furtive way and I wished now that I had never seen that room in the attic, those rumpled dirty blankets that held the coils of the serpent through the night. To pass the newly neatly-painted front of the house on the way to school was now nearly as soul-chilling as to meet Pillans himself on the road, knowing that that bright dignified frontage concealed the squalid kitchen and the more squalid room upstairs. In the old days, the house had at least looked like a lair for Pillans but it was now as if the snake had gone even further underground, presenting this new façade to the world.

'I don't see what we cleaned all that bloody furniture for,' I said to my mother, in an attempt to rouse her to anger or indignation or anything that would give me a clue to these secret thoughts of hers. 'It'll be as dirty as ever, lying down there neglected. I don't believe Castleside's going to be a shop at all. Old Pillans has been coddin' ye!'

Formerly, to suggest that anyone, even Pillans, could 'cod' successfully my mother who knew so well what was what would have created a storm of rage but now she made no response except to say quietly: 'Mr. Pillans knows what he's doing' and I felt more worried than ever. Every day now, she went out to the Secondhand at about nine-thirty in the morning, came home for half-an-hour in the middle of the day and then went back and remained there until after five in the evening. On Saturdays, she was there sometimes until nearly midnight. There were few patrons of the Secondhand during the week and she amused herself by cleaning and dusting the shabby odds and ends, stopping periodically to lift the lid of the black-enamelled cash-box in the drawer and count the few coins it contained.

Watching her, one afternoon, a horrible thought crawled out of the dark depth of my mind like a sinister worm. My mother was planning to steal some of old Pillans's wealth. My breathing became constricted with the horror of it and I now began to watch her more carefully than ever, going to the Secondhand with her and sitting in a corner much of the time. On Friday evening, I sat quietly on an old box at the back of the dim dusty cavern, looking on at the sordid little trans-actions that took place, as my mother turned another and yet another penny, some of them of doubtful honesty in my opinion, but under my keen eyes all the pennies went into the black box in the drawer and none of them into the pocket of my mother's skirt.

I ought to explain that my horror and fear that my mother might divert some of Pillans's money to her own kist were not born of the fact that this would declare her to me as a thief. My idea of honesty was similar to that of most people of the class and the place to which I belonged and this included my mother and Miss Miller although they would never have admitted it in vulgar words. As I saw it and as they saw it, people were honest until they were found out and publicly branded with dishonesty. What worried me about my mother now was not that she might embezzle a few shillings or even pounds of Pillans's money, for anyone who succeeded in doing that would have had my unbounded admiration. What worried me was that my mother seemed to be unaware of the fact that it was impossible to steal from Pillans without being found out. One might steal a letter and a book, as I had done, but these were things that Pillans would have relegated to the dustbin in any case but I knew with certainty that nobody could steal a coin, however low in value, from him without his becoming aware of it. To steal a coin from that black box would set up a reaction, I was sure, like the mysterious one set up when you pushed the little new button on the front door of Castleside and a bell rang, thirty yards away in the kitchen at the back. Take a coin from the black box and a bell would ring in Pillans's head, I knew, in his office away up in Glasgow.

Watching my mother, sure now that she was planning a theft because I could think of no other explanation of her behaviour, I could not understand how she could be so ignorant of the basic nature of Pillans. Not only would he know if she stole from him but he would also be able to produce factual proof of her stealing and then he would prosecute her without mercy. Although I knew so much about Pillans that my mother did not seem to know, however, there was no way of telling her what I knew or of warning her how dangerous was the course she was planning. I imagined trying to warn and I knew precisely how the dialogue would go.

'Ye'd better not pinch anything from old Pillans,' I would say, 'for he'll have ye in Beery-belly's cells before ye can wink.'

'Jeanie Robertson!' I could hear her scandalized shrillness. 'The impudence! *Me* pinch anything? The vulgarity! Besides, Mr. Pillans would do no such thing to me. He knows me for an honest hard-working woman.'

I could not imagine the dialogue beyond this point, for my mother would hold to things as they appeared on the surface while what I wanted to deal with was deep, deep under the surface, deep down in the mind of an orphan who wanted to be rich, have possessions and 'be somebody in the world'. Under the surface of people, I had discovered, there could be an area like Pillans's squalid kitchen and attic behind the façade of Castleside and I knew that, under her surface, my mother would steal anything if she thought that she could go undetected, impudent and vulgar as it was to say so. And I also knew that, under the surface of Pillans, there was not a single glimmer of human feeling or mercy.

My mother, I could only suppose, had become swollen-headed, because Pillans seemed to have taken her further into his confidence than he had ever been known to take anybody before. She had always prided herself upon knowing more than other people and in her conceit, I could only think, she had become blind to the fact that Pillans's mind, unlike her own, did not stop at knowing what was what but went on to what being which, why, where, when and, most important of all, how much.

About nine o'clock on that Friday evening, I was still in my place in the corner of the Secondhand, watching my mother, when I felt rather than saw the furtive movement at the back door as Pillans himself arrived. I immediately got up and took myself off quickly by the front door on to the Friday night pavement where the voice of Kingdom Come and the smell of fish and chips mingled on the breeze. I was not in the mood to join my fellows, however, but went and hid myself in the wash-house where, from my hole in the wall, I took out my new book and unwrapped it from its protective covering of newspaper. This was the first time I had seen it since the evening when I found it for I had been too intent on watching my mother to think of reading but now I sat down on an upturned wooden washtub and opened it. At the end of the first few lines, I decided that it was unconscionably dull and very unlike anything else I had ever read so, instead of going on, I went back to the page at the beginning and read the message 'To Jean, from her loving brother Charles'. After this, it seemed vulgar not even to try to read this book, although the long-ago Charles was not really my brother, so I began again and had another try.

Again, I gave up and sat with the book between my hands thinking how strange it was that this book had lain hidden for all these years until I came along to find it. I turned back to the message at the beginning, then skipped a page or two, to see if I could find a bit about the lady with diamonds in her hair or a bit about the handsome gentleman she would marry in the end, because this was the sort of rubbish that books were about mostly, unless they were about children dying with holy words and beautiful smiles on their lips. I knew that things were not the way they were in books. Everybody in books was in good circumstances, with diamonds and servants and no babies died as Mrs. Lindsay the Trammie's baby had died, choking its life away, hideously, because of diphtheria or as Marie-Bernadette's baby had died, before it was even born.

But this *Cranford* book was different. There were no diamonds in it and no holy children. It was all about a lot of old women having tea-parties and I was just about to give up for good when, at the bottom of the fourth page, I read: 'Moreover, it was considered "vulgar" (a tremendous word in Cranford) to give anything expensive in the way of eatable or drinkable at evening entertainments.' I had never before come across anything in any book that touched upon my own life so closely and I read on to the top of the fifth page. '"Elegant economy!" How naturally one falls back into the phraseology of Cranford! There, economy was always "elegant" and money-spending always "vulgar and ostentatious"——' I was uncertain of the meaning of some of the words but I was not uncertain of the truth of what I had read. This Mrs. Gaskell, I told myself, knew what was what and having been so right about vulgarity and economy, she was probably right about the old ladies and their tea parties too, difficult as it was to believe in them. With a new concentration and a will to believe what I read that I had never brought to any book before, I read on through the long June evening to the very end and when I had closed the book, I had to blink myself back from the drawing-rooms of Cranford to the wash-house of Railway Terrace.

Other books that I had read were a lot of rubbish, as I had always known and I was not prepared to believe that everything in this book was true either but bits of it were true and this was a great satisfaction. Maybe when I went to Laurelbank I would find books that were true in the glass-doored bookcase. It was silly, after all, to have expected to get the truth from the Penny Library, especially when you pinched the books and did not even pay the penny and it was sillier still to expect your mother or Miss Miller to have books that were true for 'the truth was not in a them' as old Cock was always saying about us children. I put my book back in its hiding-place and went into the house. It was nearly midnight and my mother was already undressed and sitting by the empty grate in her night clothes.

'Where have *you* been till this time o' night?' she asked angrily.

'Nowhere,' I said and began to undress and when I was in my chairbed, she said: 'How often have I told you it's vulgar to be out so late?'

'You were late yourself,' I cheeked back.

'That's different. I was out at business.' A brilliant gleam of satisfaction showed in her eyes for an instant and my stomach gave a nasty little heave. Had she gone and done it? Had she waited for old Pillans to leave the Secondhand and then pinched some of his money? 'Get off to sleep,' she said and blew out the candle.

Damn, I thought, has she already put the money in the kist? But no, she would not do that. She would be afraid that I would come in and catch her with the kist open and see all the little bags of money and the rolls of notes. I settled down in my bed, began to give my imitation of the sound sleep of the just and it was not long before she had the candle alight again and was groping under the sink for the key.

As usual, she took her skirt from the chair and her purse from its pocket and, as I listened to the chinking and rustling, there did not seem to be any more of it than usual and she spent less time this evening gloating over the bags of coins and rolls of notes already in the kist. Yet, there was something queer in the air and I remembered again that gleam in her eyes, that inward light of satisfaction. And now she did not, as she usually did, lock the kist and hide the key under the sink. Instead, she went to her coat on its hook behind the door and took a small package from its pocket. An icy shudder ran down my spine as I watched her kneel down again beside the kist in her nightgown, her back to me as she rustled the tissue paper of the package. This was it, I was sure. She had really stolen something, thinking that she was cleverer than old Pillans. Bang was going the prison door behind my mother, bang was going my job at Laurelbank, bang was going the whole future of both of us. The fool that she was, oh, the fool, to think that she could cheat the master-cheat,

Pillans. She put the package into the kist, locked it, hid the key, blew out the candle and got into bed across the room but I took a long time to go to sleep, far longer than she did.

The next day being Saturday and a busy day at the Second-hand, my mother went out at nine o'clock and as soon as she had gone, I bolted the door on the inside. I then did something that I had never done before. I took the key from under the sink and opened the kist.

I do not wish to imply that I had respected the secrecy of the kist out of any principle of integrity or regard for my mother's privacy. Until now, I had tried to ignore the kist, just as I had always tried to ignore the Iron Man on the mantel, because they were the two features of my home that represented the two aspects of my mother that I most feared and most disliked. The kist represented her economy and the Iron Man her un-vulgarity. Nor do I wish to imply that I was opening the kist now in an attempt to prevent my mother from falling upon the non-existent mercy of old Pillans for that was not the sole reason. I was opening it in an attempt to save myself from having a mother that old Pillans had sent to prison and when I thought about her pathetic stupidity, I was torn between pity and rage.

As I raised the wooden lid, my prayer was that she had kept the money she had stolen separate from the other packages and I thought that I had heard her re-wrap it in its own package the night before. Sure enough, tucked in a corner there was a small package wrapped in dirty tissue paper and, as I began to unwrap it, feeling the hard metal inside, I had a surge of relief that all she had taken was a few small coins. But the package did not contain coins. What lay exposed on my palm on the bed of dirty paper were Grammar the Belgie's ear-rings, those unmistakable pendants of gold filigree with the large oval purple stones. Stunned with non-comprehension, I re-wrapped the package exactly as I had found it, replaced it in the corner, locked the kist, hid the key and let myself out of the house to roam the streets of the town all forenoon.

After a short interval for a silent dinner with my mother, I took to the streets again, but I could not make sense of any kind of the contents of that package. My mother must have taken leave of her senses. I could understand how the pendants had come into Pillans's hands, as payment from Grammar of the rent for the Paddies, but why had my mother been such a fool as to steal something so identifiable? She could never wear the things in Lochfoot, for I and every Railie and Trammie child of my age and a little older and a little younger would recognize them, quite apart from Pillans himself recognizing them. As for selling them, turning them into money, as might be her intention, they were far too easily traceable. The only explanation was that my mother had gone mad, so mad that she had lost the inbuilt cunning which was the main survival mechanism in a life like ours.

At last I made up my mind what to do. At the next opportunity, I would get the pendants out of the kist and back to the Secondhand where I would drop them in some dark corner, of which there were plenty among all the old furniture and odds and ends. Then, when the hue and cry about their loss was raised, I would be the one to find them and restore them to old Pillans.

Unfortunately, however, I would not be able to carry through this plan until the Monday because, apart from church when I would be with her, my mother would be in the house all day Sunday. All I could do on Saturday night was to pray hard to God not to let Pillans find out that my mother had pinched the pendants which old Pillans, worse than pinching, had extorted from old Grammar the Belgie and, once again, God answered my prayer. Sunday morning dawned and old Beery-belly had not knocked on the door of Number Three Railway Terrace.

Since we acquired the mangle, we had acquired another item of furniture for the parlour, which was a wooden clothes horse in four hinged sections over which the sheets were draped after mangling but one section of it was retained for our own use. There, on two coat hangers, hung our church-going clothes, which meant that they were less creased and smelled less strongly of camphor than when they had been kept in the second kist. The church service began at eleven and when, at about ten-thirty, I came through from the parlour in my Sunday-best, my mother was doing her hair at the small mirror that hung on the window frame above the sink and I noticed, with my customary amusement, the word 'Elliman's' written across her reflected forehead and the word 'Embrocation' written across her reflected chin, for the mirror was an advertisement for this product. And then I saw Grammar the Belgie's ear-pendants lying on a corner of the table, before my mother turned round with that secretly satisfied smile of hers, picked one of them up, turned back to the mirror and began to fix it to the lobe of her right ear. There was no doubt in my mind now that she really was mad. Pillans did not go to church but dozens of people at the service would recognize those pendants.

'You can't wear these to the kirk!' I blurted out in protest and she turned round, one pendant dangling.

'Why should I not?' she asked angrily.

I could not voice the thoughts that were so clear in my mind. She looked so pathetic and innocent, standing there with one pendant dangling from her ear while she looked down at the second one between her hands. I could see behind her, where the sink should be, the grey walls of the orphanage, inside which, the older girls said, the orphan girls had their hair cut off and had to wear grey overalls that were all alike and had little to eat except bread and water. Because of all this, I could not say gently, as I wanted to say it: 'Ma, you pinched these ear-pendants from old Pillans and I know why you pinched them. They are the loveliest things you have ever touched. But, Ma, you have to give them back. He'll find out and put you in prison. Everybody in Lochfoot knows where these things came from, everybody except you, Ma. Ma, believe me, you can't get away with this!'

'Why shouldn't I wear them to the kirk?' she asked again, less angry now, her glance dismissing me as a stupid brat.

'They——' I began, paused and then blurted: 'they're vulgar!'

'They are *not*!' She was furious. 'They're *good*—real gold an' real amethysts! Mr. Pillans told me that when he gave me them last night and Mr. Pillans knows what's what.'

She turned back to the glass and began to fix the second pendant to her ear while I sank weakly on to the chair that, by night, was my bed. It was the worst moment of my life until then, that moment when my brain took in the knowledge that old Pillans, who never gave anything to anybody but always took everything away from everybody, had given my mother that pair of valuable ear-pendants. In that moment, although I could not have found words for the knowledge, I knew that the first instalment had been paid by Pillans on the soul of my mother.

I can remember every moment of that long Sunday with hideous clarity. On the way to church, as we turned the corner of Railway Terrace and Tramway Buildings, my mother said: 'I might as well tell ye. Mr. Pillans and me is getting married.'

I wanted to run, to run away back down the road, drop over the wall, run along by the sewer, throwing off my Sunday clothes as I passed along the slimy grass and emerge at last, naked, in the clean fresh world of Up-the-Burn but I continued to walk along primly, beside my honest hard-working widow woman of a mother, in my Sunday boots and cotton gloves.

'Will old—will the minister call the banns the-day?' I asked, for it was as well to be prepared for this public disgrace.

'No. We're gettin' married quiet-like in Glasgow.'

'When?'

'In a month's time.' She stepped along proudly among the

thickening crowd on the pavement as we came nearer to the church, hugging the secret which would soon be public and set Lochfoot ringing with her triumph. 'It'll be lovely to live at Castleside,' she said, 'far better than up Victoria Drive, with no neighbours to bother me. I've always liked to keep myself to myself.'

But there will be old Pillans, I thought and, as we entered the church porch, I thought of the rumpled dirty bed in the squalid attic. Would they do That in that bed? Surely not. It was ludicrous and things more terrible to think of old Pillans doing That. Did snakes do it? Or didn't they come along, slithering, find some spawn a female had laid and fertilize it, keeping themselves to themselves? I took my seat in the pew beside my mother.

The service, that Sunday, was even longer than usual for there were many announcements. Old Poopit made a long speech to the effect that we were all very vulgar and ungenerous because of the money that was still needed to pay for the war memorial and there were three lots of banns called that morning as well, which meant that we had to sing his favourite hymn in addition to all the others, but at long last we were free to go home.

Stepping carefully between the patches of fish scales on the pavement, my mother took up her conversation at the point where she had left it before church, but she was talking more to herself than to me as she walked along.

'Castleside's lovely, isn't it?' she asked at the end of a long soliloquy as we rounded the corner of Railway Terrace.

'The front of it is,' I agreed, 'but the rest of it is a dirty hole.'

'Ach, you!' she said irritably as she unlocked our door. 'When this furniture'—she indicated the contents of our kitchen—'is down in that kitchen, we'll have all we need.' Taking off her gloves, she looked up at the Iron Man. 'Mr. Pillans and I are plain folk and we'll live plain. Our private part o' the house is no concern o' the folk that come to buy furniture.' She turned to me. 'And Mr. Pillans is putting a new sink in the kitchen,' she told me with pride.

'Not before time,' I said. 'The one that's in it isn't fit for a pig's trough.'

But she would not become angry at my ungraciousness, would not begin the shouting quarrel that I felt might release some of my pent-up misery. Instead, she softened in a way that I had never seen before, became almost pleading so that I wished I could bring myself to strike her, to strike away the pathos from her voice and face as she said: 'Jeanie, Mr. Pillans has asked me down there the-night to arrange where the new sink is to go and things like that. Ye'll come down with me, Jeanie? If I go to Castleside on my own when Mr. Pillans is there, folk'll talk. Folk like her next door there are so vulgar.'

I hated myself for agreeing to go, but I had to do what she asked. 'All right,' I said. 'I'll go down with ye.'

As we sat at the dinner table, we did not talk. She had taken off her ear-pendants and they now lay beside her plate, where she looked at them with pride from time to time and it was now that I realized fully what had happened, how completely my mother was about to withdraw from me, from Miss Miller, from Railway Terrace, from the whole world of Lochfoot because she was departing into the world of old Pillans. My chaperonage of her on her visit this evening, I told myself, would be the last link between us. She had been thinking all the time, during these days when I had been so worried about her, of the grandeur of Castleside and all the money that she and Pillans would make together. When she was married to him, I felt suddenly sure now, they would not do That together when they went to bed. Instead they would talk of all the things they had bought cheap and sold dear that day and go on to plan what they would buy cheap and sell dear on the morrow before they went to sleep.

After we had our dinner, my mother sat down by the fireplace with the *People's Friend*. On any other Sunday, she would have been busy washing our clothes or cleaning the house or doing some other task that would leave her weekdays free for the mangling and the Secondhand but today, ever since she had put on those ear-pendants, she had turned into a different person. She was no longer a Railway Terrace house-wife, no longer a hard-working widow woman. She was part competent business woman, part chatelaine of Castleside. She was already the wife of Mr. Pillans, as she called him and, as such, she was taking her Sunday afternoon leisure.

My brain numb under the bombardment of strange new impressions, I left the house and without pre-planning, I found myself on the way to the Village instead of on the way to Sunday school. When I went into Lilac Cottage, my granny was sitting as usual by her fire which the June sunlight from the window had turned to feeble flames and dull grey ash and she looked round at me with a quiet smile. Standing in the middle of the floor, I said: 'Granny, my mother's going to marry old Pillans.'

She went on looking at me, her face placid and kind. 'I thought it might come to that,' she said quietly.

'She's going to live at old Pillans's place.'

'Aye. That will be so. When a woman marries, she goes to live with her man.'

'Granny, can I come down here and live with you?' My granny was silent. 'Granny, I don't want to have to live at old Pillans's place.'

'When do you start work at that Laurelbank house?' she asked.

'The first o' the month.'

'When is your mother and—when is your mother getting married?'

'In about a month's time, she said.'

'You stop with her until ye go to work, Jean. After that, when you have time off, ye can come here. That way, ye'll not have left your mother. You'll just have got separated from her in the way o' the world.'

'I see,' I said. I felt better. My granny was so wise. I did not want to abandon my mother entirely but I did not want to have any truck with old Pillans's place. My granny had shown me how to drift away without a quarrel, how to compromise 'in the way of the world'.

'It takes all kinds to make a world,' my granny said next, 'and it's a blessing they don't all want the same things. It'll be fine to see ye here on your days off, Jean. Go an' make a drop o' tea for us, lassie.'

I filled the kettle, put it on the fire to boil. 'Granny, who *is* Pillans?'

It was strange, I thought, that I had never asked her this before. If anybody in Lochfoot knew about Pillans, it would be my granny. Yet, it was not strange either that I had not asked. I had never before wanted to know about Pillans. Indeed, I had actively wanted to know as little about him as possible; I had avoided the thought of him in the way that I had always crossed the street rather than pass close by him on the pavement.

'Just Pillans,' my granny replied to my question.

'There's nobody else in Lochfoot called Pillans. It's a name I've never seen in the papers. Does he belong here?'

'Does he belong anywhere in partic'lar?' my granny asked. 'But he doesna belong to Lochfoot. He came here a goodish time ago. He's about as old as myself. Aye, it was funny the way he came here, when I think on it. Castleside Farm was a bonnie place that belonged to the Wilsons for generations but the last Mrs. Wilson never had a son. Her family was all lassies, eight o' them, eight lassies. They all went out to service, of course, except the youngest one, Jessie. Then old Wilson died and it was then that Pillans came, as a ploughman ye know, to work the farm for Mrs. Wilson. A skinny customer he was, no like any ploughman that anybody had ever seen.

It was about a year, maybe a month or two more, after he came that Jessie Wilson got drowned in the Old Dam up at the Tinker Camp. It was never known just how it happened but she had aye been a quiet kind o' soul, too quiet maybe, the brooding kind, ye might say and they came to think she had done away with hersel', poor lassie. It seems she just left Pillans and her mother sitting at the fire that winter's night and went up there and drowned hersel'. After it happened, Mrs. Wilson went queer in the head and not long after, she died o' the pleurisy. It was a very hard cold winter, that year an' a lot o' the old folk went, I mind, my own gran'father among them.' My granny paused for a moment, thinking of her grandfather perhaps, but her forehead wrinkled in a puzzled way as she went on thoughtfully: 'When the other seven Wilson lassies came home for their mother's funeral, there was a lawyer came an' told them that Castleside had been left lock, stock and barrel to Pillans. There wasna a bent bawbee for any o' them. That's how it came to be Pillans's place. Did ye put any sugar in this tea, Jean? Ye did? Well, I'll take another spoonful if ye please. I seem to have a kind o' a sourness in my mouth the-day.'

I put the second spoonful of sugar into her cup and while she stirred the tea, I asked: 'And it was Pillans who sold the green field where Railway Terrace is?'

'Och, aye. Pillans sell't all the ground o' Castleside. It used to stretch from the house down to where the tramcar depot is an' up the lochside to the top o' Lochview, as they call it. Pillans would sell himsel' if anybody would buy him but nobody would, not even the Devil.'

Nobody, not even the Devil, except my mother, I thought. My granny could indicate in a subtle way that she was not prepared to say any more on a subject and I was aware now that she had spoken the last word she was going to speak about Pillans and she made no further comment on my mother's plans either.

I did not tell her of the ear-pendants that had once belonged to Grammar the Belgie because I thought she would not wish to know of my mother's new ownership of them. I felt that my granny would loathe as much as I did the devious way in which these ornaments had travelled from Grammar's ears to the ears of my mother and it was good to sit with her there in the cheerful little house where there were no Iron Men and no sinister under-currents. I stayed with her for as long as I could but in the end I had to leave her in order to accompany my mother to old Pillans's place. I did not tell my granny where I was going after I left her for there was no more point in disturbing her with this than there had been in distressing her with the story of Grammar's ear-rings. As I buttoned my Sunday coat, she said: 'A bonnie coat, Jean.'

'Aye,' I agreed. 'I got it new when we started going to the kirk.'

'I see. Aye, I thought there was something in it when your mother started goin' to the kirk. There's aye something in it when folk go out o' their ways. Well, Jean, come down an' see me again as soon as ye can manage it, lassie.'

As I walked up the road under the Castle wall, it came to me that circumstances were deeper and more devious than I had yet understood. I had been seeing my mother as the victim of old Pillans, as the prey drawn by his tentacles into his lair but this was not how my granny was seeing what had happened. But it was all too complicated to think out to the end and there was no point in thinking about it in any case. My own future was assured in that I would never have to look upon old Pillans's place as my home.

After we had had our tea, my mother and I walked, in silence, down to the corner by the sewer. To know that Pillans was waiting for us inside changed the house into a sinister trap in my mind and when my mother pushed the little button of the newly installed doorbell, I had an urge to turn and run as if for my life. The door opened and there stood Pillans, a study in black and various shades of grey. He wore a dark suit, what little hair he had was dark grey and the skin of his bald head, his face and his thin too-prehensile hands was of paler grey.

'So this is Jeanie,' he said. It was the first time I had ever heard him speak and he spoke softly, sibilantly, as if saving his voice energy for more important matters than speaking to me. He held out his dreadul hand. 'How are you, Jeanie?'

I put my cotton-gloved hand into his but I did not speak. I could not, because I was concentrating on getting my hand safely back out of his grip.

'Come in, Mrs. Robertson,' he said to my mother, 'or Ada, now that I have the privilege. It is nice of you to come down.'

My mother bowed graciously, her ear-pendants swinging, while pride in the formal unvulgarity of it all oozed from her as she stepped over the threshold. I did not follow her.

'I'll just have a walk round outside,' I said.

She turned round, Pillans turned too and they both looked out from the inner dimness at me in the sunlight on the doorstep. Then they looked at one another, decided silently that they would be pleased to be rid of me and my mother smiled at Pillans and said: 'She's a great one for poking about on her own.' She then looked at me. 'All right, away ye go but don't get your clothes dirty.'

They then shut the door, leaving me on the outside.

Behind the house, I looked through the tumble-down out-buildings of the one-time farm and then I went over to the corner of the walled-in rectangle in which the house stood and looked down into the sewer and then up its course to the iron grating that was the entrance to the world of Up-the-Burn. I wished that I was up there, sitting on my eel boulder just below the dam, with my bare feet in the clean water instead of standing here in my toe-pinching Sunday boots.

Wandering back towards the house, I heard my mother and Pillans talking in the kitchen and, keeping close to the

234

wall and out of sight, I edged towards the window with its broken pane and listened. I did this more from force of long habit than out of any desire to hear what they said. One always eavesdropped on adults and it was enjoyable when they turned round and found one listening. The strange and amusing thing was that you could always tell how ashamed they were of what they had been saying by the degree of their anger when they knew that you had heard. 'The ladies know the best about kitchens, I always think,' Pillans was saying. 'Leave such things to the ladies, I always say. Very well, Ada, they'll put the new sink just where you want it. Now, come over here. I have something to show you, something that is just between ourselves.'

Oh-ho, was it just between themselves? Was it. That is what *he* thought, the slimy old snake. Carefully, I moved to a spot where I could not only hear them but could see their shadows on the floor. There was a creak, a bar of shadow moved across the floorboards of the kitchen. He had opened the door of the cupboard in the corner where the gas meter was.

From their shadows, it looked as if they were both kneeling in front of the cupboard and I ventured to peer over the edge of the window sill. Yes. They were kneeling there, three-quarters turned away from the window and me, all their attention concentrated on the cupboard. Old Pillans tilted up the gas meter a little, eased out from under it the end of a floorboard and let the meter sink back into place before he raised the board, put his hand into the cavity and drew out a black enamelled box, exactly like the cashbox in the Secondhand. Setting it on the floor between him and my mother, he drew a bunch of keys from his pocket, opened the box and held up before her eyes a long gold chain with, here and there along its length, a pearl and on the end of it there dangled a gold watch, topped by a true-love knot of pearls.

'For you on our wedding-day,' he said, smiling a terrible long-toothed smile.

'Oh.' Had she had eyes for anything other than the jewel in front of her, she would have seen my forehead and eyes at the window, for I was looking straight at her face through the oval of gold chain and pearls that hung from Pillans's outspread, long thin fingers. But she did not see me. She looked from the watch up into his face and said: 'Are you not the fly one? I scrubbed the inside o' that cupboard an' I never knew that this board was loose,' but what she was really saying was: '*you* are so clever. Teach me to be as clever as you are.'

Smiling with his lips closed now, he accepted her admiration of him and then they both gazed rapt, transcended beyond themselves with greed, at the chain, the watch, the knot of pearls while I slipped down below the level of the window and crept away along by the wall. I felt giddy, as if I had been swinging round and round one of the clothes-poles in the backyard of Railway Terrace for a long long time and I could hear inside my head the voice of Doris: 'Jesus! The greed, the bliddy greed! In the name o' the Kingdom o' Heaven, if there's one thing I canna abide, it's greed!'

Over in the corner by the wall, looking down into the sewer again, I saw my mother and Pillans, as if they were reflected in the black water, kneeling on the floor with the black box between them, as if they were praying by some altar, their faces adoring as they gazed at the swinging jewel and in my buzzing giddy head I seemed now to hear the hymn we had sung in church that morning, the wedding hymn that began with the words: 'O Perfect Love——'

CHAPTER TWELVE

Yes, we'll gather at the river,
The beautiful, the beautiful river,
Gather with the saints at the river
That flows by the throne of God.

REDEMPTION SONGS 664

WHILE I WAS EATING MY PORRIDGE the next morning, my mother said: 'Don't you go blethering about Mr. Pillans and me outside, mind. We want to keep our business to ourselves. It'll be time enough for folk to know about us when we put the marriage notice in the *Leader*.'

Gone was the tentative pathos of the day before. She spoke with a brave new authority, as if the coming marriage were now a certainty in her mind while, yesterday, it had still been a dream, as if, indeed, that sacrament of avarice over the enamelled box on the floor of the squalid kitchen had been the sacrament of marriage between her and Pillans.

'Don't worry,' I told her. 'I won't be telling anybody.'

The coming union was not something about which I wanted to boast and I was sure that my granny would not boast about it either.

'Mr. Pillans is not coming down here again now until after we're married,' she said. 'As he says, you can't be too careful in a place like this with all the vulgar talk that goes on.'

The dreadful respectability of it all threatened to stifle me, so I decided to go to school that morning, to the familiarity of the stale-smelling classroom where there would be no lessons because, since the rebellion, we simply refused to co-operate if old Cock tried to take a lesson, although we would sing 'Onward! Christian soldiers' with gusto if he chose to rehearse us and quite often of our own volition if the mood came upon us.

237

As I sauntered down the road past the pub, I was joined by wee Sammy Gardiner who, in his tribally uneducated way, looked up at me and said: 'I'm glad you're coming to the school the-day, Jeanie. I've been missing ye, Jeanie.'

'Ach, give it a bye,' I said but I slowed my step so that he could limp along at my side.

Behind us, just as we came to the corner of the road to the Village, there was a sudden stampede of Trammie boys, led by Tom Telfer and as they rushed along one of them knocked against wee Sammy so that he lost his balance and fell against the wall. Before I had even thought, I had stuck out my foot as Tom Telfer rushed past me, bringing him down headlong on his face into the gutter. Blood dripping from his mouth and chin, he dragged himself up on to his hands and knees, a fearsome sight as his glaring eyes fixed on myself. There was a nervous tittering that died into silence as Tom got to his feet and came at me. I tried to defend myself and wee Sammy, courageously, was doing his best, banging at Tom with his crutch but neither he nor I would have survived had not the voice of authority come from the Village road: 'Telfer, let Jeanie Robertson be!' and there was Ian Adair, to whom Colin had relegated me when he went to the Academy two years before. Ian was about five years younger than Tom but of about equal size and he was also backed by his brother Peter, the little boy who had played on the floor with red bricks on that day long ago while, behind the Adairs, came the brawny might of all the Villagers, boys and girls. The fight grew from more or less single combat between Ian and Tom into a full-scale battle in which my part was to try to screen wee Sammy from the mêlée, holding him behind me while kicking out at anyone I could reach. Soon, every Railie, Trammie and Villager was in the fight, its origin forgotten by some and unknown by others, a good three hundred of us, packing the width of the road in a punching, clawing, kicking, scratching mass while the publican and a few other adults looked on helplessly. Suddenly, wee Sammy slipped out from behind me, swung his crutch and clouted Tom and Ian one after the other on their heads with the padded part that went under his arm while his voice rose above the din in a shrill desperate scream: 'It's old *Pillans*!'

There was a silence and stillness of death before the publican retired into his doorway, the other adults drifted away and all of us children backed away across the road towards the Castle wall, leaving the pavement clear for the bowed figure in the bowler hat and long black overcoat to pass like a phantom, close to the wall of the pub and the shops. When it had disappeared round the corner of Railway Terrace, I discovered that Sammy and I were pressed back against Tom and Ian who towered above us. Tom looked down at me and wiped the blood from his chin with the back of his hand. 'If ye trip me again,' he said, 'I'll have yer guts for garters, so I will, ye wee bitch.' And then, 'Come on, Adair,' he said. 'Race ye to the school gates!' and they both went tearing off down the road towards the school.

As I walked slowly along with wee Sammy, a whole set of circumstances came together in my mind like the steel snakes of the railway lines going together at the end of the siding. Grammar's watch was down under the floor at old Pillans's place, Madame Fenchel's address was in my notebook in the wash-house and the big brass key of Pillans's front door was hanging by the window in our kitchen, that my mother might admit the plumbers to the house when they came to fit the new sink. I stopped walking, put my hand on wee Sammy's shoulder and said: 'I'm not coming to the school. I've changed my mind.'

'Aw, Jeanie!'

'Shut up. I'll be there at the interval. I've got something special on an' you're in it, Sammy. If anybody asks ye, say I've been at the school all the time.'

He looked up at me proudly. 'Right, Jeanie. I'll say that ye were at the school right from Bible the whole day.'

'That's right. See ye at the interval,' I told him and ran back to Railway Terrace.

The key of our house was under the doormat so that I might let myself in at dinner-time if my mother was not back from the Secondhand and having taken the brass key from beside the window, I pushed both keys up my knicker leg. If my mother came home unexpectedly and found our door key gone, I would meet that hazard when I came to it but it was essential that she should not get into the house to find the brass key missing. She glanced proudly up at that key every few seconds.

As I came out round the corner of the Terrace, I could hear the school bell ringing in the distance and now the street was deserted. It was too early for the shoppers to be abroad and all the workers were already at the tramway depot or the railway siding. I ran fast down to Pillans's place, like a child late for school, slipped quietly across the yard and in through the new, easy-to-unlock easy-swinging front door. It did not take a moment to get the floorboard up and although the black box was heavier than I had expected it to be, I soon had it out of the hole. After a few seconds, the cheap lock broke under the leverage of the kitchen poker but when I opened the lid, my hands were arrested. The box contained not only Grammar's watch. This lay on top of a lot of dirty little tissue paper parcels like the one that had contained the ear-pendants. I began to open some of them. There were rings, bracelets, lockets and chains, brooches —one brooch in the shape of a big pointed star and set with glittering white stones which could only be diamonds, like those worn by the ladies in the books I had read. The box was a veritable miser's hoard.

The sight of it all made me so angry that my hands shook as I wrapped Grammar's watch and chain in a piece of the

240

dirty tissue and pushed it up my knicker leg. There was an old piece of sacking in the bottom of the cupboard and, spreading it on the floor, I heaped all the jewellery upon it, turned the box upside-down over it to shake the rest of the parcels out and then I tied the sacking up in a rough bundle. I put the broken empty box back into the hole where it looked as if it had never been touched and replaced the board, edging the end of it carefully in under the heavy gas meter. I then let myself out of the house, setting the heavy little sacking bundle on the doorstep while I locked the door and replaced the key in my knicker leg. The road was deserted as I went out of the gate, the sacking bundle bulging the front of my jersey. At the bridge at the end of the wall, the black water of the sewer was flowing silently into the conduit pipe under its scum of yellow froth. I dropped the sacking bundle in. There was a break in the froth, a black bubble rose and burst its slimy skin and Pillans's treasure was gone. I ran home and replaced the keys, but I did not risk going down the yard to my wash-house hole with Grammar's watch. Close to the wall of the Terrace, I was safe enough from Miss Miller's eyes but if I went away from the wall or showed my head above her window sill, she would see me in the mirror of her sideboard-if-you-please. I was back at school well before the forenoon interval and sang 'Onward! Christian soldiers' in rehearsal with the package that held Grammar's watch pressing comfortably against my leg.

It was not until I was in my chairbed that night that a new aspect of my morning's work struck me. What a joke it would be if, when Pillans found his black box empty, he thought that my mother had pinched his hoard. After all, this would be the logical thing for him to think, for it was unlikely that he had shown that hole and the box to any-body else. But next I remembered that my mother had told me that he was not coming down to Lochfoot again until after they were married and this made the possibilities to accrue from my expedition funnier than ever. While my mother undressed modestly in the dark, I could barely refrain from laughing aloud. There they would be, till death did them part, wondering what each other had done with the contents of the box, for my mother would be sure to think that Pillans had regretted promising her the watch and that he had taken it away to his office in Glasgow.

Soon it was the last Saturday of June, the day of the Unavailing and, as I got up that morning, I thought it would be easy always to remember the happiness of this day. I had finished with school for good the afternoon before, there was the Unavailing today as if in celebration, then there would be the short No-man's-land of Sunday before, on Monday morning, I would be turned into a fully-fledged member of the adult world.

The strange thing was that I did not feel any different. I had no desire, as the other big girls had, to tell the younger ones to stop doing this and not to do that. The way Millie Greig went on at wee Annie Murphy the day before about peeing behind the wash-house being dirty and disgusting, you would have thought that Millie Greig had never pee-ed anywhere except in the proper place all her life when everybody knew that Millie Greig's one claim to fame had been her ability to pee at any time, anywhere, when such a leaving of the tribal mark of protest had been deemed necessary. In the name o' the Kingdom o' Heaven, Millie Greig was the one that pee-ed in the Co-op man's milk can the morning after he had given Jimmie Anderson a leathering for raking in the dustbin! But Millie seemed to have forgotten all that since she grew up and never wanted to go Up-the-Burn or anything nowadays.

For myself, I had every intention of taking a final trip Up-the-Burn before I went away to Lochview on Monday. There had been some rain lately and the Burn was lovely when it was in slight summer spate, especially up at the Dam where the water poured over the concrete rim and down into the Burn like a glass curtain with a deep white frill of foam lace at the bottom. I intended to go up on Sunday, not even come home for my tea and have something to look back on when I had gone to Laurelbank.

The Unavailing began with all of us of the choir being lined up in twos in the school playground, where old Cock gave us a lecture about behaving ourselves, while the rest of the school, who should not have been there at all because it was Saturday and who were there precisely because they should not have been there, looked in at us forty through the railings from the road, giggling and shouting rude remarks. Then we forty were marched down through the town to the memorial, while all the others came rioting along behind but Beery-belly and Macaroni chased them away behind the big crowd of adults who were standing all round. I found my spot on the tram-line and looked about me. The Unavailing, I knew, was something to do with the war, like a thing called 'Armistice Day' that we had had back before the New Year. Armistice Day took place in the school playground and we all had to sing a hymn, standing in the rain, while old Cock stood with his watch in his hand. Then we had to bow our heads and stand still and silent for two minutes and it seemed like forever before old Cock put his watch in his pocket and started to pray. After that, we went back into school again and two of the boys got a leathering because they had been kicking a stone to and fro to one another instead of standing still and silent as they had been told to do.

As I looked around me, the Unavailing looked as if it were going to be a more cheerful affair than Armistice Day. Everybody was there, old Loco, old Squeak, old Stink and Lewie Leadpipe in their Sunday suits and I could see my mother and Miss Miller over to one side in their Sunday hats. The memorial itself looked very gay too, for it was covered from top to bottom in a huge Union Jack and in the recess inside the iron railings, the brass band stood in a semi-circle around it. Their instruments gave off flashes of light for, although it was a cloudy day in the main, there were blinks of sun.

The gaiety of the big flag and the brass band made me remember Doris and her gramophone, with the record of the band of the Irish Guards playing a waltz out into the street through the pink horn while Doris sat at her open window singing: 'Where the blue Danube flows along—' but the memory picture faded away as a big black car drove right into the middle of the crowd. Beery-belly tried to pull his stomach in as he saluted and opened the door of the car, out of which came old Poopit and a lady and gentleman dressed all in black. The brass trumpets and trombones stopped flashing as the sun went in and the air became grey and chill. The big flag hung limp and everybody became dead quiet, bowing their heads as old Poopit began to pray.

As the ceremony went on, it grew more and more dreary. Although, when old Poopit stopped praying, everybody sang a psalm, they sang sadly and a lot of women were crying even while they sang. I felt my stomach getting cold, not only with disappointment but because of the weary dreary unavailingness of it all. I had been looking forward to our singing 'Onward! Christian soldiers' and everybody clapping when we finished but now I knew that there would be no clapping and I wished it were all over. At last, it was. The lady in black, who had a white handkerchief in one hand, had a rope put into her other hand by old Poopit and when she pulled on the rope, the Union Jack came tumbling down as if by magic into a ring round the bottom of the stone pillar. I looked upwards from this gay garland to the flat bronze panel with the columns of names, up again to the top of the rough stonework and up again and there was my father, standing on top of the pillar, my father in the kilt with the apron over it, the cape round his shoulders and the steel helmet on his head, but he was all made of iron. From the boots and puttees to the top of his head, they had turned my father into an Iron Man and as I looked up at his unseeing eyes, one of the bandsmen began to play long sad notes on a bugle. At this, I too began to cry, to cry for my father and because I could not run away from this terrible thing, trapped as I was by iron railings, stone walls and people.

At last the crowd dispersed, old Cock disappeared into it and Beery-belly told us children to get away home out of it and I ran all the way back to Railway Terrace. My mother must have taken the key to the Unavailing with her for it was not under the mat, so I had to wait for her to come before I could change out of my Sunday clothes. Quite soon, she and Miss Miller came round into the yard, their voices sharp with disapproval as they came.

'To think of what it cost!' my mother was saying. 'All that money for *that* thing! Did ye see the big tear at the side o' the man's cape an' the other one on the knee o' the trousers?'

'Aye an' the lump o' mud on the boots,' said Miss Miller. 'Imagine putting a thing like that, right at the station where it's the first thing any stranger to the town will see! Surely they could have made the soldier look clean and tidy?'

'Vulgar, I call it,' my mother pronounced the final verdict. 'Just plain vulgar!'

I changed my clothes in the parlour with my back to the mangle and when I came out through the kitchen, I was careful not to look at the mantel for I could not bear to see another Iron Man.

'Here, you, where are you going?' my mother asked.

'Mind your own business,' I cheeked back and ran out of the house, the close, the yard and on to the street.

Down at Pillans's corner, the Burn was sliding down into the pipe and I stayed watching it for a little while, for long enough to let the postman cycle up as far as the pub before

I would drop over the parapet but now wee Sammy came limping down the road.

'Jeanie,' he said, pleading eyes looking up, 'you're goin' Up-the-Burn. Take me wi' ye, Jeanie!'

'Away home an' boil yer can, ye silly wee thing,' I told him.

'Aw, Jeanie, I was nine last week. Ye know that. Folk gets to go Up-the-Burn when they're nine. Folk are not in it till they've been Up-the-Burn.'

'Don't be a stupid wee fool,' I said angrily, shaking his hand from my old skirt. 'Ye know fine I canna take ye up there. What if old Stink caught us?'

'I can run, Jeanie! Look!' He went hobbling away across the road and while his back was turned I dropped over the parapet on to the slimy grass. As I ran along under the wall, I heard his voice: 'Aw, Jeanie, take me wi' ye!' but I kept running on. But after I had crawled through the iron grating and was in the magic world on the other side, I was still haunted by wee Sammy. I could see him limping away from the bridge, past old Pillans's place and back to his home. Sammy with his crutch, his steel brace on his leg, would never see this world of amber-clear water rushing over clean stones under the sprays of wild roses. Maybe I should have brought him, taken the risk of old Stink, who was probably still down in the town in any case, in the pub discussing the war memorial with his friends.

I squatted on my eel boulder while the water rushed gurgling past me, remembering the first time I had come up here, the many other times I had come to catch eels for Madame Fenchel, to pick flowers for Doris but behind everything there were the pleading eyes of wee Sammy, the pleading voice saying: 'Take me wi' ye, Jeanie. Folk gets to go Up-the-Burn when they're nine. Folk are no' in it till they've been Up-the-Burn.'

I had meant to roam all over the forbidden territory that day until the memory of the Unavailing and everything connected with it were entirely blotted out but I did not roam. I sat on my eel boulder for most of the afternoon, thinking not of the Unavailing but of wee Sammy which was even worse, wee Sammy who, because of what the steamie had done to him, could never be in it. I should have brought him with me but I would make it up to him. Suddenly, I made up my mind. I would go right back to the Terrace and organize a special expedition for the next afternoon, a Sunday, the last day before I went to work and joined the adult world. Tom Telfer would help. Tom was a decent sort if you treated him properly and remembered his position as Trammie Leader and he would get one or two other big boys to help us to get wee Sammy safely over the parapet and in return I would give them my precious secret. I would show them how to drop out over the wall into the school playground or at any other point they pleased.

It was queer, I thought, how I had been the only one to come to know that there were so many ways out of the land of Up-the-Burn although there was only one way in. The others always came back by the way they had gone, through the grating, along by the sewer and up over the parapet at Pillans's corner. Thinking of how I would impress Tom and the other few chosen boys on the morrow, thinking of the pleasure of showing wee Sammy the waterfall at the Dam, I felt better and swinging my feet in the water, I began to hum my favourite hymn:

> By cool Siloam's shady rill
> How sweet the lily grows!
> How sweet the breath beneath the hill,
> Of Sharon's dewy rose!

This was my song of Up-the-Burn and I always thought of this place when I sang it, even in the classroom or in church. It was queer too to think of going to work on Monday. It was queerer still to think back over all the years, back to the time when I did not know that this land of Up-the-Burn existed. Time was so long, when I looked back and I began to wonder how long Railies and Trammies had been coming up here. For as long as Railies and Trammies had existed, I supposed, since just after the Terrace and the Buildings had blotted out the green field. These early Railies and Trammies had handed on their knowledge of how to get Up-the-Burn in spite of all the walls and gates and railings and it was right that I should hand on the discovery I had made, the knowledge that although there was only one way in, there were many ways out. I stood up on my boulder and, springing across to the bank of the Burn, I headed through the woods to the point where the Castle wall ran along the back of the school playground. If I had to find Tom Telfer and organize wee Sammy's expedition for the morrow, it was time that I was back in the streets and backyards.

I went home and had some tea first. My mother was round at the Secondhand, so I ate nearly all of the loaf that I found in the cupboard for, after all, when Monday came, she would not have to feed me any more. I then set out to find Tom Telfer, which took some time for he was a very elusive person. I ran him to earth at last among a pile of boxes in the back-yard of the Arms, where he was filling a sack with empty beer bottles to sell to one of the other pubs on Monday evening.

'What the hell *you* doin' here?' he whispered at me angrily.

'I'll give ye a hand,' I whispered back and helped him to get the full sack over the wall but when we had stowed it safely among the rubble in a corner of Sandy the Tinker's burned-out house, Tom was not at all co-operative with my plans for wee Sammy's expedition of the next day.

'You an' Davie Murray an' me would be enough,' I argued. 'It's only to get him over at Pillans's an' through the grating. After we're up there, you an' Davie can go off on your own.'

'But he's such a *wee* smout an' he's that bloody lame,' Tom objected. 'What if old Stink——'

'Old Stink my behind! It'll be Sunday an' he'll be readin' his Bible.'

'Aye, Sunday,' said Tom, 'an' old Pillans'll be at his place an' we'll get seen!'

'Old Pillans will *not* be there. He'll be up in Glasgow, my ma said and *she* knows.'

For once, my mother's association with old Pillans was of some use.

'And listen, Tom, I can show you an' Davie something up there that nobody knows but me.'

'What?'

'D'ye think I'm tellin' ye for nothing? D'ye think I'm daft? But, listen, if you help Sammy an' me the morn, I'll show ye. Honest, Tom. Cut my throat if I tell a lie!' I made the tribal gesture of drawing my forefinger across my throat and spitting on the ground.

'Right, ye're on,' said Tom suddenly, 'but mind, if you're tryin' to cod me, Jeanie Robertson, I'll murder ye, so I will!'

'I'm not coddin' ye, Tom. It's something great, what I can show ye, honest it is.'

'Right. And just Davie an' me an' you an' wee Sammy is in it, mind. Davie an' me'll see ye at old Pillans's at two o'clock the morn.'

All I had to do now was to find wee Sammy and apprise him of the great news and, unlike Tom, wee Sammy was always easy to find. He did not move far from the door of the cobbler's shop or the door of the pub unless I took him somewhere special. As I made my way along the street, it was a typical Lochfoot Saturday night. It was about ten o'clock, several people were already drunk, the fish and chip shop was busy and belching a cloud of blue smoke across the pavement and my mother was doing a brisk trade at the Secondhand. As I went round the corner of Railway

Terrace, I could see ahead of me the Salvation Army band, shaking the spit out of their trombones at the pub door while Kingdom Come lectured the unheeding air about hell-fire.

'Sammy!' Mrs. Gardiner was calling on the pavement. 'Samm-ee!'

I was just in time. Unlike most parents in our part of the town, Mrs. Gardiner tried to have Sammy in bed by ten o'clock in the summer and even earlier in winter.

'Hello Jeanie,' she said to me, 'have ye seen Sammy?'

'No, but I'll get him for ye, Mrs. Gardiner.'

'He's a wee rascal. He goes and hides at bedtime.'

'Sammy!' I called up the pub close. 'Sammy, it's Jeanie. I've something to tell ye!'

There was no answer and I went, still calling, back up to the Terrace in case he had gone into our yard to look for me. On the way, I met Beery-belly and Macaroni on their Saturday night round of the pubs but I did not find Sammy. Still calling, loud above the voice of Kingdom Come, I came back down the street and coming up the road was a band of Tinkers on their way to the pub. After the fire at the Terrace, they had taken to the open road for a time but they were now back in their former encampment at the old Dam. One of them was carrying a stick, with a piece of cloth on its end, against his shoulder as if it were a gun. At the door of the pub, Mrs. Gardiner pounced upon him, dragging the stick away from him.

'Where'd ye get that?' she shouted fiercely.

'Now then,' boomed Beery-belly, 'we'll have no fightin', if ye please.'

'It was in the Burn, doon at the brig, Missis,' said the Tinker, peaceably enough.

'Oh, my God!' said Mrs. Gardiner.

It was then that I saw that the stick was wee Sammy's crutch and when she turned it right way up, the piece of cloth flapped over, showing that it was attached to the pad that went under Sammy's arm by a big star of white stones that flashed in the light from the pub door.

I was first down at the bridge at Pillans's corner but Beery-belly, Macaroni and Mrs. Gardiner were close behind me and soon there was a crowd as big as there had been at the Unavailing, a crowd just as silent, while Beery-belly and Macaroni dropped over the parapet as if they were embarking on an expedition Up-the-Burn. Suddenly the silence was broken by the band of the Salvation Army up the road, starting to play one of its noisy and vulgar hymns, as my mother called them.

> *Shall we gather at the river,*
> *The beautiful, the beautiful river,*
> *Gather with the saints at the river,*
> *That flows by the throne of God?*

Down below, Macaroni, the black water and yellow froth lapping round the thighs of his dark blue trousers, lifted the little body clear of the slime, the little leg with the heavy brace hanging limply down, as he handed wee Sammy to Beery-belly on the bank of the sewer.

> *Yes, we'll gather at the river—*

the band played on as Macaroni climbed up, then bent over and took Sammy from Beery-belly down below.

> *The beautiful, the beautiful river—*

played the band as everybody stared and Mrs. Gardiner sobbed, banging her fists on the stone parapet.

> *Gather with the saints at the river—*

the tune floated through the twilight while the silent crowd began to walk slowly up the road behind Beery-belly who was carrying Sammy.

said the band and fell silent while I stood, alone now, where the wall of Pillans's yard joined the parapet of the bridge and the windows of his house, shining dimly in the last light, looked down at me like unseeing eyes.

Inside my head, I was facing the fact that I had killed wee Sammy. It was so easy to see what had happened. Wee Sammy had been waiting at the bridge for me to come back, for he did not know that I did not come back from Up-the-Burn by that route. The piece of sacking with the diamond star attached to it must have floated to the surface and Sammy, leaning over the parapet, had begun to fish for it with his crutch, as we all leaned over and fished with sticks if we saw anything interesting down below there. But Sammy, for ever ineducable in the laws of the child tribe, the first of which was survival, had over-reached himself and had fallen over.

It was I who had put the glittering bauble in there, it was I who had refused to take wee Sammy Up-the-Burn with me and it was I who had killed him. I stayed there by the parapet for a long long time, until it was quite dark, for I did not want to see anybody on my last journey down to the police station where I would tell Beery-belly what I had done. They would hang me up by the neck until I was dead, but I deserved it. I shivered as I watched the moon disappear and show and disappear again between the wind-blown clouds until at last the Salvation Army band stopped playing and the window-lights of the town began to go out. I walked up the road and through the quiet streets to the police station.

It was a grim grey building with two doors opening straight from the pavement at the top of some steps. There was a big double door in the office part which had bars on the windows and an ordinary door in the house part. It stood by itself, this building, with a narrow close going up one side to the main street and a road going in at the other side through a gate and round to the backyard where the cells were. The office part was all in darkness but there was a chink of light showing at the edge of a blind, upstairs, in the house part. There was a brass bell-pull in the stonework at the side of the house door and there was a dark metal knocker as well, fixed to the wood of the door itself. Shaking all over, I put my hand on the brass knob of the bell, then looked up undecidedly at the knocker. In a sudden gleam of the fitful moon, I saw that the knocker was an Iron Man, a little old iron man with a leering wrinkled face, a pointed hat and a beard. Cloud covered the moon again, making of the knocker an indeterminate shape and now, from across the street a little way off, there came a furtive shuffling movement close to the wall. I shrank against the stone at the side of Beery-belly's door as I watched old Pillans, a phantom shadow among the other shadows, shamble past under the Castle wall. He had not been able to stay away from his lair, I thought. He had had to come back to take a look at his miser's hoard.

The moon came out from behind the clouds and the whole world and the inside of my head and the inside of my breast were suddenly filled with a brilliant white light.

I had not killed wee Sammy. There were a million things in the death of Sammy. Castle walls, my mother, Doris, the Belgies, my father, Iron Men, myself, the steamies, my granny, Mrs. Gardiner and all of Lochfoot and all the world were in it, all chained together by the moving snake of circumstance that made its hidden way through the shadows of life like old Pillans. I now discovered that, when the brilliant light broke over me, I had inadvertently pulled on the brass knob of the bell and that, at this very moment, the heavy feet of Beery-belly were pad-padding towards the inside of the door. I dodged off the step and round the corner into the narrow close. The door opened, casting a shaft of yellow light into the street. I broke into a loud jeering laugh and ran away up the close. This was a matter for pride, if you please, I told myself as I turned the corner into the yard of Railway Terrace, something that no child in Lochfoot had ever done. In the name o' the Kingdom o' Heaven, I had gone to Beery-belly's very own door and there, I rang the bell, the door opened and I ran away.